Radio Shack®

Auto Radio
INSTALLATION GUIDE

Auto Radio Installation Guide
ISBN 0-8019-7297-3

CONTENTS

Chapter 1 Choosing a Replacement Radio 1

Chapter 2 Radio Installation 17

Chapter 3 CB Radio and Antenna Installation 32

Chapter 4 OEM Radio Removal 53

Domestic Cars 56

Import Cars 81

Trucks and Vans 93

Glossary 100

SAFETY NOTICE

Proper service and repair procedures are vital to the safe, reliable operation of all motor vehicles, as well as the personal safety of those performing repairs. This book outlines procedures for servicing and repairing vehicles using safe, effective methods. The procedures contain many NOTES, CAUTIONS and WARNINGS which should be followed along with standard safety procedures to eliminate the possibility of personal injury or improper service which could damage the vehicle or compromise its safety.

It is important to note that repair procedures and techniques, tools and parts for servicing motor vehicles, as well as the skill and experience of the individual performing the work vary widely. It is not possible to anticipate all of the conceivable ways or conditions under which vehicles may be serviced, or to provide cautions as to all of the possible hazards that may result. Standard and accepted safety precautions and equipment should be used when handling toxic or flammable fluids, and safety goggles or other protection should be used during cutting, grinding, chiseling, prying, or any other process that can cause material removal or projectiles.

Some procedures require the use of tools specially designed for a specific purpose. Before substituting another tool or procedure, you must be completely satisfied that neither your personal safety, nor the performance of the vehicle will be endangered.

Although information in this guide is based on industry sources and is as complete as possible at the time of publication, the possibility exists that the manufacturer made later changes which could not be included here. While striving for total accuracy, Chilton Book Company cannot assume responsibility for any errors, changes, or omissions that may occur in the compilation of this data.

1

CHOOSING A REPLACEMENT RADIO

Buying a car stereo or stereo system is not without its problems. Replacing the factory equipment AM radio with an AM/FM stereo casette and a couple of replacement speakers is not severely complicated. But, just like replacing the tired factory system with a mega-buck component system that will sound like the New York Philharmonic is in the orchestra pit under your dashboard, they both require some careful planning and thought.

The only way to be sure you're getting what you want is to learn as much as possible about the various components and equipment so that you can make the wisest investment at the lowest cost.

PRICE

Price is important. Decide how much you want to spend on the complete system, before buying any part. Since any components that you buy must be compatible, there is little point in spending too much on a tuner or amplifier and leaving insufficient funds for compatible speakers. Likewise, there is little point to forking over big bucks for an expensive integrated system that will blow the factory speakers out of the dash.

The basic component system—tuner/tape deck, amplifier and speakers—should allow approximately 45% for the tuner/tape deck, 25% for the amplifier and 30% for the speakers. This will give you a well-balanced system and the piece of mind that your components are compatible from a quality standpoint.

Naturally, your decision will also be influ-

enced by the relative performance specifications of similarly priced equipment. See the section on Specifications later in this chapter.

TYPE OF EQUIPMENT

In-Dash vs. Under-Dash

For most cars, in-dash installations are best. There is a greater variety of high quality equipment, and the factory-installed look of in-dash equipment makes it less subject to theft, more attractive and will give the car a greater resale value.

Unfortunately there are some cars in which the installation of equipment with the performance and features you may desire will be extremely difficult, if not next to impossible.

Basic in-dash AM/FM replacement radio

AM/FM stereo radio with 8-track tape designed for in-dash installation

Basic FM tuner designed for under-dash installation

AM/FM/Stereo Cassette

There are basically 3 situations where an under-dash installation rates serious consideration:
- If you own a very small import car which does not have room for an in-dash stereo of the performance that you desire;
- If you already have a system in your car or truck, with which you are satisfied, and you simply want to add the capability to play tapes;
- If you have to leave your vehicle in areas where the ONLY prudent thing to do is to take the audio equipment with you if you expect it to be there when you get back.

AM, AM/FM or AM/FM Tape

In general, AM (amplitude modulation) has a greater range than FM (frequency modulation). AM can be heard as far away as 200–300 miles from a strong station at night, but suffers from several disadvantages.

First, even though AM stations can be heard at great distances, as the station gets weaker, the volume falls off. Second, AM stations are more susceptible to interference from power lines and other man-made sources, especially when only distant stations are receivable. Traffic lights, electric signs and thunderstorms can make AM unlistenable.

FM radio is often called line-of-sight," because the high frequencies will not bounce off the atmosphere like AM radio. Consequently, the range of FM radio is extremely limited compared to AM radio—only 35–50 miles, depending on terrain. A mountain can easily block out an FM radio wave, but in downtown urban areas, the FM signal will bounce off buildings, making FM reception possible when AM is impossible.

Because more information is carried in FM stereo waves than in monaural FM broadcasts side effects such as Flutter, Cancellation and Capture are even more noticeable, and the FM stereo noise-free broadcast range is approximately five miles less than that of monaural FM radio.

FM flutter is the pops and hissing bursts heard in the speaker, during an otherwise good broadcast. Usually this condition exists while traveling in the fringe area of a station. The signal loss will become greater as you drive farther from the station, until finally noise takes over and you can no longer receive the station. Flutter may also be noticed near the station because of the "line-of-sight" characteristics of FM radio waves. This condition can happen when a building or large structure is between you and the station you are trying to receive. Some of the FM signal "bends" around the building, but certain spots have almost no signal. Some of these losses are only a few inches wide and if your car is parked in one of these "dead spots" you will only hear noise from the speaker. As you move out of the shadow of the structure, the station will return to normal. Flutter will not occur on AM, because the radio waves are much longer than FM waves.

Another effect caused by the FM "line-of-sight" characteristic is called cancellation. This condition exists when the radio waves are reflected from objects or structures. The noises produced by cancellation are similar to flutter, with the addition of distortion in the program. A more familiar description of cancellation is its similarity to the multiple ghosts and picture jumping that occur on television when a low flying plane passes. The same condition exists in your car, except that your car is moving and the reflecting structure is stationary. The reflected signal cancels the normal signal causing your antenna to pick up noise and distortion. Cancellation effects are most prominent in metropolitan areas, but can also become quite severe in hilly terrain and depressed roadways.

FM capture is an unusual condition that occurs when traveling in the vicinity of a broadcast tower. If you are listening to a weak FM station, when passing the broadcast tower, a stronger station up or down the radio dial may "capture" the weak station. This switch to the stronger station occurs without changing the radio dial. As you pass the tower, the station may switch back and forth a few times before returning to the station that you were listening to originally. When several broadcast towers are present (common in metropolitan areas) several stations may overload the receiver resulting in considerable station changing, mixing and distortion. Fortunately this condition is localized and it will not harm your receiver. Some overloading (two stations received at the same time) may also be noticed on AM when driving near towers, but usually to a lesser degree.

Located within a few feet of your highly sensitive radio is your automobile's electrical ignition system. The high voltage of this system produces noisy side effects that can interfere with both AM and FM stations. Although precautions have been taken in the manufacture of vehicles to minimize ignition noise, a certain amount can be heard on FM when the station is not quite tuned. Ignition noise from passing vehicles can occasionally be heard if they do not have proper suppression equipment installed. Various solutions to the problem of suppressing electrical interference are discussed in a later chapter.

Though it is not static-free, FM is less susceptible to static interference. Like AM, it will pick up electrical disturbances, especially when operating in the fringe of a station's receiving area. But, unlike AM, as the station gets weaker, the volume will stay the same, although background noise will increase.

Basic under-dash 8-track stereo player

Under-dash stereo cassette player

Many people invest in an AM/FM/Tape combo and never use the tape section. It could save you a considerable portion of the expense if you take a good look at your listening habits, before forking over the dough for something you don't need and won't use.

However, the modern car stereo is an extension of the home audio system, and many people like to listen to commercial-free or prerecorded music. If your preference runs to tapes, cassettes represent a higher level of technology than 8-tracks. The cassette's tape is ½ the width of the 8-track and moves at ½ the speed. They are more easily stored and have become the most-used form of tape in car stereo. Eight-tracks are still available and will give completely satisfactory service for those with a large 8-track library.

"Mini" or Full-Size

In a way, radios have been down-sized, just like cars. Many subcompacts and a few compact and mid-size cars are engineered and packaged so efficiently that a normal-size car stereo simply will not fit. Most radio manufacturers have solved this problem by making high quality, "mini" stereos that will fit both foreign and domestic cars and trucks where under-dash space is limited. An alternative is to consider a under-dash or component sys-

In-dash AM/FM stereo radio with casette player

An equalizer can be added between the front end and the amplifier to break sound into different bands

tem if you can't get an integrated system with the features and performance that you desire.

All-In-One (Integrated) System vs. Components

Integrated or "all-in-one" systems consist of a preamp (with volume, tone and other controls), a tuner (to receive AM or FM broadcasts), possibly a tape deck, and amplifier, all enclosed in one housing. Most integrated units are installed in the dash or under the dash. Hook up the speakers, antenna and power lines and you're ready to listen.

Car stereo has increasingly taken the component approach to offer even higher quality auto sound. The component approach separates the preamp, tuner and cassette deck (known as the front end) from the amplifier. The front end is contained in the same kind of housing as a traditional integrated stereo, but the amplifier is contained in a separate

An integrated system combines the amplifier, tuner and tape deck in a single housing

Component systems use a separate amplifier, tape deck and tuner. Components are not limited to size and can be larger, more powerful and of better quality

housing, located anywhere that is convenient and connected to the front end by wires. Speakers are then connected to the amplifier. An accessory, known as an equalizer, can be added between the front end and the amplifier to break the sound into different bands (usually 3–7). The bands can be controlled in loudness allowing better control over the reproduced sound.

Since the amplifiers' quality is not limited by the size constraints of an in-dash installation, it can be considerably larger and more powerful than any in an integrated system. Likewise, since the amplifier is removed from the front end-housing, the components of the front end—preamp, tuner and tape deck—can be larger and of better quality. The higher quality possible with a component system translates into cleaner sound (when reproduced through high quality speakers). Disadvantages of the component approach are greater expense and probability of a more complex installation.

Shop for components or integrated receivers in the same manner. Set your budget, then determine what will fit in your vehicle. Choose your features and power requirements. But, if you like your music loud or must have truly superior fidelity, consider components. You can create your own hybrid system, but buying all your equipment from one manufacturer's product line will assure you of complete compatibility among all system components.

FIT/INSTALLATION

Theoretically, it is possible to fit any radio into any dashboard. Practically, however, the best thing to do if you want to be sure of fit is to

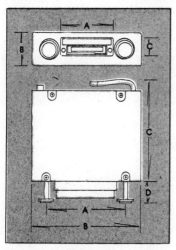

Critical radio fit dimensions: top: A-width of nose-piece; B-housing height; C-shaft hole size; Bottom: A-distance between shaft centers; B-housing width; C-depth of housing; D-shaft length

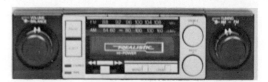

Radio Shack equipment incorporates the popular features available on quality equipment

measure the available spaces that are available to you.

Remove the existing radio and measure the space behind the dash. Measure the existing radio, particularly noting the dimensions of the nose piece and distance between the control shafts. Sketch the radio and its peculiar dimensions and use this information to make sure that a replacement radio will fit in the dash. In many cases, you can bring your car to the store, minus the radio and be sure of a good fit.

In most cases, an installation kit is either necessary or will make the job much easier and duplicate the factory look. The kits are mechanical adaptors' that allow mounting of aftermarket radios in virtually any car or truck. Most kits contain custom faceplates, replacement control knobs to duplicate the factory look, spacers, nosepiece gaskets, wires, mounting brackets and hardware and of course, instructions. The exact make-up of each kit for each individual car will vary.

FEATURES

Tuner

The tuner is the part that receives the AM or AM/FM broadcast signal. These features directly affect tuner performance.

LOCAL/DISTANCE SWITCH

If you happen to be very close to a broadcast tower, the signal could overload the tuner and cause distorted sound. Putting the switch in the "local" setting will reduce the level of the incoming signal, preventing the tuner from overloading.

MONO/STEREO SWITCH

Stereo requires a stronger signal than mono, to be heard clearly. As you move farther away from a station, the signal's strength drops. You will begin to hear hiss and noise instead of a clear signal. By switching to mono, you will again enjoy a clear signal, however, without the benefit of stereo. A few units are now being manufactured with automatic filter circuitry that blends from stereo to mono, but only to the degree necessary to maintain a clear sound.

PUSHBUTTON TUNING

If you are constantly checking out the programming on available stations, pushbutton tuning is almost a necessity and could be considered a safety feature.

Mechanical pushbuttons, require more effort to operate and will not always arrive directly on the center of the channel. Electronic pushbuttons are easier to operate (require less effort), are more accurate and are usually found on more expensive sets. They also offer the disadvantage of being less convenient to operate, frequently requiring the driver to take his eyes from the road to hit the right button.

SEEK/SCAN TUNING

When activated, a "seek" tuner will automatically progress down the dial, until it comes to the next listenable station where it will stay, until the operator activates the "seek" again.

In the "scan" mode, the tuner will automatically progress down the dial to the next listenable station. "Scan" tuning differs from "seek" in that the "scan" mode will stay on the next listenable station for 3–5 seconds, then progress to the next station, until the operator locks it in on a desired station.

MUTING

Muting does not allow the tuner to play weak, distorted stations and eliminates the irritating noise frequently heard between stations when tuning.

DIGITAL DISPLAYS

Digital displays are usually found on tuners with electronic front ends (those with "seek/scan" tuning or electronic pushbuttons. Digital displays give a much more accurate reading of the station's frequency and allow more precise calibration.

DIGITAL TUNING

Digital readouts are normally found on only the most expensive tuners. The advantage of such sophistication is more precise tuning.

The job of the tuner is to receive the exact transmitted frequency of the station you wish to hear. It must pick this signal out from all the other frequencies that are bouncing around in the sky. If the station is not accurately tuned on the dial, the proper signal will have a difficult time getting through. On a conventional tuner, rotating the knob often will not get you to the exact spot for optimum reception. The digital readout at least allows you more precise control over the exact spot on the dial that will get you the best reception. Digital readout is not a substitute for quality components or circuitry, but it is a control to aid in tuning.

HANDS-ON USE

Look for a unit whose capabilities are excellent, but also take the time to judge the in-use engineering of the unit. Placement of controls, layout of switches, size of knobs, easily visible markings, etc. all contribute to an enjoyable listening experience. Test the controls in a dimly lit room, as this will closely approximate night driving conditions. If you can easily manipulate the controls under these conditions, you should have no problem during the day.

Also evaluate the placement of controls in relation to your chosen mounting location in the vehicle.

AMPLIFIER/PREAMP

These are the controls that determine sound quality, including the volume and balance controls, found on every set.

TONE

The most common tone controls are those that simply reduce the high frequency sound level. More sophisticated and expensive equipment has separate controls to raise or lower the base and treble sound levels.

The ultimate in tonal control is a separate equalizer (which may also use a booster amplifier). The equalizer divides the sound into anywhere from 5–9 parts, any or all of which can be raised or lowered in volume to compensate for listening environment or real or imagined deficiencies in the programming.

FADER

The fader control is a switch to vary the front to rear balance of 4-speaker systems.

LOUDNESS

The loudness switch accentuates low and high frequency sounds to compensate for low listening levels.

BI-AMP

Before considering bi-amping on a stereo system, be aware that bi-amping requires that both the stereo and the speaker system be designed for bi-amping. Bi-amping is the process of sending bass (low) signals directly to the woofer portion of the speaker and treble (high) signals directly to the tweeter portion of the speaker. This eliminates the need for a crossover system in the speaker and generally produces cleaner low, middle and high frequency sound.

Pre-amp jacks are a useful feature if you ever wish to expand the system

PRE-AMP OUT PUT JACKS

Pre-amp output jacks on an integrated (all-in-one) receiver means greater versatility. An integrated system can be expanded later on as your needs and pocketbook dictate.

The pre-amp jacks allow the integrated receiver's internal amplifier to be connected to a component main amplifier at some later date. At that point, your integrated receiver will become a front end for a component system, with all the benefits of cleaner sound that a component system is capable of providing.

Tape Deck

Every basic cassette unit will have at least a manual eject—a button you push to eject the cassette. In addition there are several other eject features worth considering.

AUTO EJECT

Auto eject will automatically eject the tape when it comes to the end of one side. A variation on this theme is auto eject when the power is turned off. The main advantage to the latter is that the tape is never left in the deck while the unit is off—a definite faux pas in caring for tapes and equipment. Leaving the tape in the machine can cause the tape transport to jam when power is turned back on.

AUTO REVERSE

Instead of having to manually eject the tape, flip it over, and reinsert it to play the other side, auto reverse does this automatically. The player reverses itself and begins to play the other side when it reaches the end of the previous side.

AUTO REPLAY

Auto replay will begin to play the same side over again, as soon as the tape reaches the end of the rewind cycle and the tape is fully rewound.

LOCKING FAST FORWARD

Locking Fast Forward is a great convenience when you're trying to locate a particular portion on a tape or when you want to play the other side. It eliminates the need to hold in a rewind or fast forward button for an entire side of the tape.

DOLBY NOISE REDUCTION

Delby noise reduction is a process named after its inventor, Ray Dolby, to lower the "hiss" heard on prerecorded cassettes and certain FM broadcasts. To be effective, the tape must be recorded with Dolby noise reduction equipment or the FM broadcasts must be using the Dolby noise reduction process.

The best way to decide if the Dolby feature is worth your investment is to try it and see. If you have access to Dolby stations in your area or to Dolby tapes and your listening environment is a quiet car with loud music, you may be a candidate for Dolby. At the other extreme, if you're in an older, noisy car with the windows frequently open, and you have no Dolby stations in your area or have no access to Dolby tapes, it probably is not worth the investment.

TAPE EQUALIZATION

There are 4 basic types of cassette tapes in common use today—(1) low noise (known as normal or ferric tape), (2) chrome, (3) ferrichrome (a mixture of normal and chrome) and (4) metal (or metal particle)—each with its own unique properties and characteristics. The stereo's tape equalization circuitry adjusts the player for different kinds of tape, to get optimum playback efficiency.

The tape setting for different kinds of tape is measured in microseconds. Normal tape uses the highest setting (around 120 micro-

Radio Shack Chrome Tape is designed for use in recorders and players with tape equalization

seconds). Chrome tapes, which are generally of higher quality with lower noise, metal and ferrichrome tapes all use a setting around 70 microseconds.

Almost all tape players without a tape equalization adjustment are preset for normal tapes. Use of chrome or ferrichrome tapes in these sets will only result in a very slight shrillness, which will probably not even be heard in a vehicle environment where the audio system will have to compete with other noises such as wind and road noise.

HARD HEADS

The tape player playback heads are made of materials suitable for replaying normal tapes. The abrasive surfaces of chrome and ferrichrome tapes can cause extreme wear on playback heads designed for normal tapes. The "hard head" refers to the permalloy or sendust alloy material used to manufacture playback heads that can resist wear from chrome and ferrichrome tapes, while at the same time giving superior playback characteristics compared to normal playback heads.

UNDERSTANDING SPECIFICATIONS

Manufacturers of car stereos have agreed upon a somewhat uniform set of standards for measuring auto stereo performance. However, industry standards still leave a good deal of room for optimistic performance spec's,

while still being within industry standard guidelines.

It still remains for the buyer to compare units based on similar specification standards and to select wisely. The following is a guide to units of measurement found in star stereo specifications.

Tuner Performance

POWER

In car stereo, power is the energy that the stereo sends to the speakers. Power is measured in WATTS, but power alone is not the key to a good stereo. Power, in watts, should also be related to a given level of distortion, (THD, or Total Harmonic Distortion) since power accompanied by excessive distortion would produce unlistenable sound. Twenty watts of power is certainly sufficient to power most speakers, but if the distortion content of that power is nearly 20%, it will sound objectionable, indeed unlistenable. However, at 4 watts power, the distortion level might only be 15% distortion, a level that even the most discerning audiophile would have trouble hearing, providing the sound is put through appropriate speakers.

A distortion level of 3.5% or less for integrated receivers and 1% or less for main or booster amplifiers for quoting power capabilities will assure you of a quality sound system. Tests indicate that these are the levels at which a typical car stereo listener can identify distortion as an irritant. The considerably lower level for component amplifiers is necessary because the booster amplifier adds its own distortion to the integrated receiver's distortion.

No discussion of power or distortion is fully meaningful unless it involves speaker efficiency. For a short course in speaker efficiency, read the section on Speakers in this chapter.

SENSITIVITY

Sensitivity (sometimes called IHF useable sensitivity) measures the lowest signal level that the receiver will be able to convert into a listenable sound. The unit of measurement is the decibelfemtowatt, which represents the signal strength entering a tuner from a standard 75 ohm impedance car radio antenna, although it may be measured in microvolts. There are 2 sensitivity figures—one for mono and one for stereo—and they are important, particularly if you want to listen to a station that is far away.

An acceptable sensitivity figure for mono is in the range of 15 dBf (decibelfemtowatt) (1–5 microvolts at 30 dB). The lower the number the better. This will produce mono reception with a medium amount of background noise.

The second sensitivity figure is for stereo and should be in the 35–42 dBf range (5–10 microvolts at 30 dB)—the lower the better—to produce stereo reception with a quiet background.

AFC (AUTOMATIC FREQUENCY CONTROL)

The AFC on FM receivers tunes in and locks onto the station you want, as accurately as possible. If the AFC is too narrow it will easily lose stations. If the AFC is too wide, it will lock onto unwanted stations. The tuner's AFC specification may not be listed, but if it is, a band width of ± 300 kc (kilocycles) is good.

PLL (PHASE LOCK LOOP)

PLL electronically compares the incoming signal with a self-generated signal to keep the receiver locked onto the incoming signal. PLL is good to have and is found on many quality sets.

AGC (AUTOMATIC GAIN CONTROL)

The AGC and the "local/long-distance" switch perform similar functions.

AGC automatically improves adjacent channel rejection in areas where signal strength is high. Weak signals are gained, but strong signals are not. A 50 dB AGC rating is good and the higher the number, the better the AGC circuitry.

FREQUENCY RESPONSE

The overall sound spectrum is generally accepted by 20–20,000 cycles per second, measured in Hertz (Hz). A set with good frequency response will be capable of reproducing sound from the 50–15,000 Hz range, which is approximately the range of a typical FM station. The wider the specified frequency response range, the better the set.

SEPARATION

Stereo separation is the ability of the tuner to capture the broadcast signal on the right and left-hand channels and make it play out the right and left-hand speakers, respectively. The separation specification, expressed in decibels (dB), is the difference between the channels. The higher the number, the better.

Tape Performance

Specifications of tape player performance apply equally to cassette or 8-track units. There are basically 3 specifications of concern.

WOW AND FLUTTER

Wow and flutter is the ability of the tape transport to move the tape over the heads in a smooth, uniform manner. Wow refers to long variations in tape speed and flutter is the measurement of short variations. They are commonly expressed as a combined percentage of deviation from what is considered to be perfectly smooth movement. A figure of .25% is good and the lower the number the better.

SIGNAL TO NOISE RATIO

This is the measurement of how much louder the signal on the tape is, compared to the noise of the tape itself, known as hiss. An average signal to noise ratio is 50 dB. Noise can be heard at this level, but it is not annoying to the average listener, and between 55 and 60 dB, noise ceases to be a factor. The higher the number, the better.

Sets with Dolby noise reduction circuitry can have as much as an extra 5–10 dB of signal to noise ratio, when a Dolby tape is played. Be sure to check if the specifications given are with that circuitry in operation.

FREQUENCY RESPONSE

This is very similar to FM frequency response, described under Tuner Performance. Good reproduction is from 50–15,000 Hz, and the wider the range, the better.

SPEAKERS

Speakers are one of the most neglected components of a car stereo system. You can have the best component audio system available, but without good speakers, it won't take a bit of difference, because poor speakers create their own distortion and static.

There are several factors that should be considered in your speaker decision.

Fit

First, you should determine where you are going to place your speakers in the vehicle. This will go a long way toward narrowing your choice of speakers.

Car speakers come in 2 basic mounting types—flush mount or surface mount. Flush mount, also known as recessed, work best in doors, kick panels, rear quarter panels, or rear decks, where they produce the best sound and are out of the way. The large open areas in doors and under the rear deck (below or behind the speakers) serve as acoustic enclosures, reinforcing the bass tones. Flush mount speakers are usually round or oval shaped.

Surface mount (wedge or hang-on) speakers come with their own enclosures, usually made of high strength ABS plastic. They are quickly and easily installed on almost any

SPECIFICATIONS—WHAT THEY MEAN

dB (decibel)—A unit of measure used for describing the relative intensity of sounds or signals. A three decibel increase equals a doubling of power. For instance, if four watts produce a sound level of 90 dB, eight watts would be required to produce a sound level of 93 dB. Sixteen watts would yield 96 dB, and so on.

dBf (decibelfemtowatt)—A unit of measure for the signal strength entering a tuner from a standard 75 ohm impendance car antenna.

Efficiency rating—Designated as high, medium or low, the efficiency of a speaker is directly related to the sound pressure level (SPL) that can be produced from a reference level signal. For example, one speaker may produce 94 dB SPL from a one watt signal. This would be a "high" efficiency. Another speaker may produce 88 dB at one watt. This speaker would be termed "low" in efficiency.

FM frequency response—This refers to the total sound spectrum from low to high frequencies that the tuner is capable of reproducing Factory radios typically respond from 100 to 10,000 Hz or less. A response of 50 to 12,000 Hz is considered to be full range. Units with the capability of 30 to 15,000 Hz will capture all frequencies that can be legally broadcast.

Hz (Hertz)—A term that expresses frequency in cycles per second and is used in place of this older term (cps).

Impedance—Generally, a measure of electrical resistance which is given in ohms. A four ohm speaker has less resistance than an eight ohm speaker and is therefore considered more efficient.

Monophonic usable sensitivity—Expressed in dBf (decibelfemtowatt) this is an indication of the weakest signal with which the tuner can produce a listenable sound. An acceptable figure is 20.0 dBf and anything under 15.0 dBf can be considered excellent.

Monophonic 50 dB quieting sensitivity—Also expressed in dBf (see above), this is the signal level required to achieve a 50 dB signal to noise ratio. Anything under 25.0 dBf is acceptable by today's standards. Under 20.0 dBf is excellent.

Power output—Due to variations in the different manufacturers' specifications, we have chosen to continue testing power output in our own lab facility. Integrated receivers are rated with a 1000 Hz signal input for maximum power in watts at 3.5% THD (Total Harmonic Distortion). Our independent tests have indicated that most people begin to perceive distortion at this 3.5% level. Compo-

Typical flush-mount speakers designed for door panels or other panel installations

flat surface and can even be installed beneath the dash if they are attached to a flat board.

The mounting location you choose will usually determine whether flush or surface mount speakers will be used. Speaker location is critical. Tweeters are highly directional and should be mounted facing passengers, close to ear level. Mid-range speakers are less sensitive to direction and can be installed lower in doors or kick panels. Woofers are the least sensitive to direction and can be placed virtually anywhere. Surface mount speakers are the easiest to install, but flush mount speakers produce better sound. The bass response in particular, is superior due to

nent or main amp amplifiers are rated with a 1000 Hz signal for maximum power output at 1.0% THD.

Recommended minimum load—For an amplifier to operate correctly, it must have a proper "load." The load is provided by the speakers, which are rated in ohms (see impedance). Depending on how many speakers are used, and the method selected for wiring them into the system, the *combined* load can vary. For example, a unit has a recommended minimum load of four ohms. Two pairs of four ohm speakers are to be connected. If the speakers are wired in parallel, the combined load becomes two ohms—if this were used it could damage the amplifier due to the increased current flow. Series wiring, on the other hand, would result in an eight ohm load, which is safe for the amplifier. Our trained staff will gladly assist you in making the wisest choice for your application.

Signal to noise ratio—Expressed in dB (see decibel) this is how much greater your program material is than the residual *electrical* noise level of the circuitry and/or mechanism. A 40 dB S/N ratio means that what you want to hear (your music) is 10^4 times as great as what you don't want to hear(noise). A 60 dB S/N ratio means that a signal is 10^6 or one million times greater than the noise. Obviously, the greater this figure, the better.

Stereo separation—This refers to the ability of a tuner to take the right channel broadcast material and make it play out of the right speaker and vice-versa for the left channel. Expressed in dB, the figure given is how much greater the signal is from the designated channel than the opposite channel.

Tape frequency response—This is the range of the sound spectrum which a unit is capable of reproducing. The figures given by manufacturers are dependent upon the test tape which was used and, in some cases, the actual tape formulation plays a large role. For example, Jensen rates their units to 10,000 Hz because that is the limit of the laboratory test tape they used. Jensen units *will* reproduce frequencies considerably higher in actual consumer use. Similarly, the Concord units achieve greatly extended frequency response by using state-of-the-art metal particle tape formulations.

THD—Total Harmonic Distortion represents the percent of distorted content an amplifier is producing at the given power output.

Wow and flutter—This is a mwasure of tape speed variation. Expressed in percent the lower this figure the better.

PLEASE NOTE: *The specifications in the charts shown in* **bold face** *type were determined in the Crutchfield Testing Laboratory.*

Basic surface mount speakers in ABS acoustic enclosures

High quality, surface mount speakers using woofer, tweeter and cross over network in one housing

the larger area behind the speaker that serves as a baffle.

Before you begin cutting holes for speakers, check the 5 critical speaker dimensions shown in the drawing. Accurate measurements are crucial. Double-check all your dimensions. When dealing with interior volume measurements of a speaker enclosure (such as a car door), remember that air must circulate around the speakers. You should also make a few other checks. Will the speaker's location effect the operation of window crank, convertible top mechanism or spare tire re-

moval. If yes, find another location. Also, probe around, removing a few pieces, if necessary, to be sure there is enough room to fit the speaker where you want it. Operate any functioning components to be sure that sufficient clearance is present at all times.

Types of Speakers

Functionally, automotive speakers come in many types. Single cone speakers use only one sound producing surface to reproduce the entire range of sounds. Multiple driver systems use separate speakers to reproduce different sounds. Woofers reproduce the bass tones, mid-range speakers reproduce the middle tones and tweeters reproduce the high sounds. Multiple driver systems always use

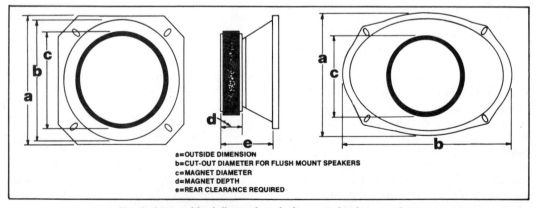

a=OUTSIDE DIMENSION
b=CUT-OUT DIAMETER FOR FLUSH MOUNT SPEAKERS
c=MAGNET DIAMETER
d=MAGNET DEPTH
e=REAR CLEARANCE REQUIRED

Check these critical dimensions before purchasing speakers

5", single-cone round speaker

6" x 9", single cone oval speaker

6" x 9", oval coaxial speaker

6" x 9", oval tri-axial speaker

A woofer, mid-range and tweeter enclosed in a single housing

some sort of cross–over network to divide the range of sounds and send them to the appropriate speaker to be reproduced. Other multiple driver systems separate the drivers entirely and mount them in different locations.

The most popular automotive sound systems use speakers known as coaxials or triaxials. Basically these speakers consist of a midrange and treble driver mounted on a plate in front of the woofer. Another variation is the tweeter mounted in front of a combined bass/midrange driver.

More sophisticated variations on a theme are subwoofers, specialized speakers that use their own amplifiers. Because these speakers reproduce the very lowest ranges of bass, below the range of conventional woofers, they often have their own level controls for smooth sound output. Directly related to subwoofers are biamplified systems, which use a separate amplifier for each speaker, in addition to separate level controls for each driver. They also use a cross-over system installed before the amplifier stage and separate power amplifiers for each driver.

Amplifier Compatibility

Consider the compatibility of the amplifier and speakers. The power coming from the amplifier should not exceed the speaker's rating, although the speaker's rating can be greater than the amplifier's power.

Efficiency

Speakers in a car or truck environment often have to overcome outside noises, so they should be capable of playing loudly with a minimum of input power. An actual specification for the efficiency (sensitivity) of a speaker is hard to get sometimes, because many manufacturers don't quote it, or quote it differently. A speaker that has an efficiency of more than 90 dB for one watt at a distance of approximately 1 yard is good. In practical terms, a low efficiency speaker will require somewhere around 20-plus watts to produce clean sounds at reasonable sound levels. Medium efficiency speakers will require 10–20 watts and high efficiency speakers will need 3–10 watts to do the same job.

Be sure that you check the output of the set before choosing speakers. A low output amplifier should not be used with low efficiency speakers. Bass will be practically nonexistent and you won't be able to play anything loudly.

STEREO

Stereo equipment (radio or tape) requires the use of at least 2 speakers to achieve the stereo effect, although you could use 4 or even 6. But, no matter how many are used, remember that stereo separation must be side-to-side.

ANTENNA

No matter how good a stereo you buy, it will only be as good as the signal that it gets through the antenna. For best AM reception, you should use an antenna extended as high as possible, but FM reception requires an optimum height of 31 inches. This also works well for AM and is the optimum length because it represents ¼ of the FM wavelength.

There are several types of antennas. The traditional extendable antenna is seldom seen anymore, giving way to the 31 inch, one-piece whip antenna. These are probably the best compromise, as they stay tuned for FM reception and offer the most resistance to casual vandals who like to break the antennas off of parked cars.

The windshield antenna supplied with many new cars works well with AM, but leaves something to be desired for FM.

For those to whom price is no object, or who fear the car wash gremlins and want to be able to retract the antenna out of sight, power antennas that are activated by turning the radio ON or OFF are the only choice. Some incorporate an amplifier in the base of the antenna to boost the radio signal. Some of the signal in any antenna is lost through the cable before it reaches the receiver. The booster amplifies the signal before it reaches the cable, enabling a stronger signal to eventually reach the receiver. Some electronic antennas offer another advantage—they are shorter and designed to operate on ⅛ of the FM wavelength. Their masts can be set at only 15 inches, compared to the conventional 31. You should decide on the power antenna feature early in the game. Not all tuners have provision for power antennas, and if none is present, a separate switch will have to be used.

CAR SOUND CHECKLIST

Tuner/Tape Player

- In-dash mounting is best
- AM/FM/cassette tape player
- Does it fit the space available?
- The tuner/tape deck should cost 40–50 percent of the total you can spend
- Is it styled to blend with the dash

Tuner

- Are the controls easy to use

SPECIFICATIONS

- IHF useable sensitivity: FM sensitivity of 1–5 mv and stereo sensitivity of 5–10 mv at 30 dB, AM sensitivity of 20–25 mv at 20 dB (lower is better)
- Image rejection ratio or band selectivity of 40 dB (higher is better)
- "Local/Distance" switch or automatic gain control of 50 dB (higher is better)
- Stereo separation of 25 dB at 1000 Hz (higher is better)

• Frequency response of 50–15,000 Hz (broader is better)

FEATURES

• Pushbutton tuning (nice, but not at the expense of audio features)
• Digital or continuous readout (no performance difference)
• Electronic tuning (no performance difference)
• "Muting" switch
• "Mono/stereo" switch or automatic switching circuit
• "Loudness" switch
• Power antenna lead
• Separate bass and treble controls
• Balance control, side to side
• Fader control, front to back
• Preamp Output Jacks (necessary for the best quality sound)

Tape Player

• Cassette player (unless you already have an eight-track library)
• Front or side load (no performance difference, side load has less frontal area)
• Chromium dioxide metal tape capability (nice, but not necessary)

SPECIFICATIONS

• Frequency response of 50–15,000 Hz (broader is better)
• Wow and flutter of 0.25 percent (lower is better)
• Signal-to-noise ratio of 55–60 dB (higher is better)

FEATURES

• Power off/eject
• Auto-reverse (no performance difference)
• Locking fast forward and rewind
• Dolby noise reduction (necessary for the best quality sound)

Amplifier

• Separate component amplifiers usually give better sound
• Amplifiers are better than power boosters

• The component amplifier should cost 25–30 percent of the total you can spend
• Is amplifier compatible with tuner for impedance and input sensitivity
• Will it fit in my car
• Biamplification (requires 4 speakers)

SPECIFICATIONS

• Average power output per channel of 15–20 watts at 1 percent total harmonic distortion (higher output is better, lower distortion is better)
• Signal-to-noise ratio of 70 dB (higher is better)

FEATURES

Internal short and overload protection circuit (absolutely necessary) Automatic power equalizer

Equalizer

• Integral with amplifier or separate (be wary of getting a power booster instead of a true amp)
• Will it fit in my car
• The equalizer should cost about 5–10 percent of the total you can spend
• Is it compatible with my amplifier and speakers

SPECIFICATIONS

• Frequency bands adjustable to ±12 dB

FEATURES

• Five to seven band equalization
• Balance control, side to side
• Fader control, front to back
• Dual amplifier fader (necessary in a two-amp biamplification system)

Speakers

• Will they fit in my car
• Is the total speaker system compatible with my amplifier for power handling capacity (cautious types will get speakers rated for slightly more maximum power than the amplifier)

• The speaker system should cost 25–30 percent of the total you can spend

• Is the total speaker system compatible with the amplifier for impedance

• Are the speaker grilles styled to blend with my car

SPECIFICATIONS

• Frequency response of 60 to 18,000 Hz (broader is better)

FEATURES

• 20 ounce magnet or smallr "super magnet" on woofers

• Foam or cloth hinge

• Acoustically neutral speaker grilles

Antenna

• Will it fit on my car

• A manual retractible antenna can cost less than $5, a signal-boosting or automatic power retracting antenna will cost about $50, a power retracting signal-boosting antenna is $100

• Is it styled to blend with my car

• Is it made just for AM/FM

SPECIFICATIONS

• The best antenna is a signal-boosting electronic antenna, next best is a 31 inch whip, everything else is third

FEATURES

• Automatic power retracting (requires a power antenna lead on the tuner)

2

RADIO INSTALLATION

The relative ease of installation of your car stereo will be a direct result of the decisions you made when determining what pieces would fit in your car or truck.

Nearly anything can be made to fit, given enough time, money and ingenuity. Fortunately, there are custom installlation kits and pieces available for most of today's vehicles and these will make the job infinitely easier. It is impossible to give a complete guide to installing radios in every vehicle in this space, but the following general tips and hints, along with the basic procedure will smooth all but the most complex installations.

There is little doubt that most installations can be accomplished by the average owner in a minimum amount of time with a minimum of problems and fuss. Do-it-yourself installation is basically a matter of minimal technical expertise, simple car mechanics and common sense.

SAFETY

1. Disconnect the negative battery terminal before beginning the removal and/or installation process. This will prevent shocks from any exposed wires, run-down batteries due to lights left on and doors left open and the possibility of damaging components by connecting the wrong wires.

2. Always protect your eyes with goggles when using power tools or when there is possibility of flying projectiles or material removal.

3. Cover your seats and interior with a blanket or heavy material and keep tools out

RADIO/TAPE PLAYER/SPEAKER INSTALLATION CHECKLIST

The following basic outline will guide you through the installation process. Planning is as important as learning as much as you can concerning your system. This book will help you with the learning process, but you should also talk to the audio salesmen and installers where you buy your equipment. They will be able to offer invaluable tips from their own experience. Likewise, most manufacturers employ service and technical representatives who can answer any of your questions relating to their specific equipment. Study the instructions supplied with your equipment and follow them carefully.

- Draw a Diagram
- Assemble the Materials
- Check Both Systems for Proper Function
- Disconnect the Battery
- Remove the Existing Radio
- Make Final Measurements
- Install the New Radio/Tape Player
- Connect power to the Radio/Tape Player
- Connect the Ground wire to the Radio/Tape Player
- Install the Speakers
- Connect the Speaker Wiring
- Recheck all Connections and Installation
- Connect the Antenna
- Reconnect the Battery
- Test System for Proper Installation

Disconnect the negative battery terminal before beginning any work

of your pockets. This will protect both you and your car's interior from damage.

4. Take your time. Patience and care is a good portion of the job and rushing things can lead to accidents as well as mistakes. Remember that your car or truck and new stereo system represent a substantial investment. Plan the time it will take according to the complexity of the job. Don't try to install an entire system in a few hours in the morning. Allow yourself plenty of time.

5. Be sure that you have everything that you will need assembled before beginning.

6. Read everything before starting the installation.

TOOLS

Installing a super-expensive component system where speaker enclosures have to be fabricated will frequently require a number of specialized tools ranging from power bench saws to power routers.

The average installation requires surprisingly few specialized tools. Most of the tools you'll need are those that can be found in the ordinary handyman's collection. The rest can be begged or borrowed from friends or acquaintances. The list includes:

1. A handful of assorted wrenches both sockets and box/opened—you'll need American or metric sizes depending on the origin of the car you're working on.

2. Screwdrivers—both large and small, flat blade and Phillips.

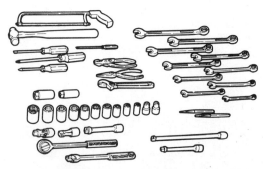

Common hand tools are normally necessary for most installations

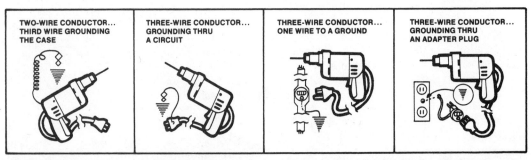

When using electric power tools, be sure the tool is properly grounded—preferably by a 3-wire connector

3. Wire stripper or combination wire stripper/crimper.

4. An electric drill—the common ¼″ type is best.

5. An assortment of drill bits.

6. Black electrical tape and masking tape.

7. Pencil, compass, piece of chalk.

8. Razor blade—the single edge kind is the safest and easiest to use.

9. A round and flat file.

10. A keyhole saw or hole cutting attachment for the electric drill.

11. A selection of male and female spade connectors, and other terminal hardware. Optional equipment includes a soldering gun, solder, flux and a combination volt-ohmmeter. These last items may come in handy for solving specialized problems and for checking continuity, but in general, you won't need to have them on hand before you begin.

12. Pliers—both slip-joint and needle-nosed.

13. If you are installing speakers in the doors of a GM car, you'll need the handy little tool for removing the window cranks so that you can remove the door panels. These can be purchased at most auto parts stores inexpensively.

One other item you may want to consider is a service manual for your vehicle, to guide

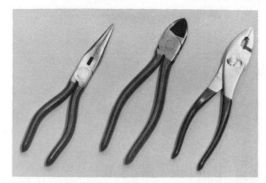

Several kinds of pliers will be necessary

you through the temporary removal or disassembly of unfamiliar parts of your car or truck. Radio, speaker of antenna installation may require any of the above for proper installation.

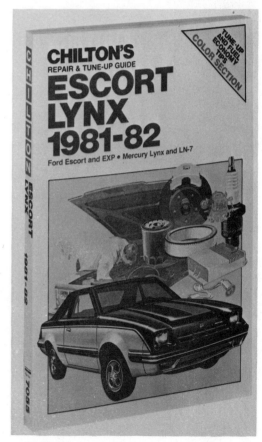

CHILTON'S
REPAIR & TUNE-UP GUIDE
ESCORT LYNX 1981-82
Ford Escort and EXP • Mercury Lynx and LN-7

TUNE-UP AND FUEL ECONOMY TIPS
COLOR SECTION

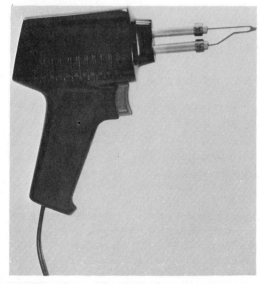

Soldering gun is necessary for soldering connections

A service manual for your vehicle will help with the removal or disassembly of unfamiliar components

DRAW A DIAGRAM

It is always helpful to draw a diagram of the planned installation and refer to it often during the installation process. The diagram should include the color coding of wires and their function, their planned use in the final installation, their connection to other wires on the radio and any other peculiarities of your system. Check the diagram against the manufacturers instructions, and in the best of all worlds, have someone else go over the whole thing to make sure it is done properly.

If you are installing a component system, the diagram should also include such details as the location of components, as well as how they will be wired into the complete system.

ASSEMBLE THE MATERIALS

Gather together all the materials, parts, pieces, tools, instructions and anything else that you feel you might need. Don't worry—you will always find that there is some tool that you have to go and get—no one ever anticipates all the eventualities. Be sure that you understand everything involved in the job and have read and understood all of the instructions.

CHECK BOTH SYSTEMS

First, check the existing radio/speaker/antenna combination for proper performance. This way, you'll know that if the new system doesn't work after it's installed, the problem is in the installation or the new equipment.

The new equipment can also be eliminated as a cause of any problems, if it is bench tested (temporarily hooked up to speakers, wired and played) prior to installation.

DISCONNECT THE BATTERY

After testing the existing system, disconnect the battery negative cable. This is both a safety precaution and insurance against running the battery down by having doors open or lights on for extended periods of time.

REMOVE THE EXISTING RADIO

If you haven't already done so, push the seat all the way back. Radio removal procedures for the original factory installed equipment are covered in Chapter 4 of this book. Refer to these procedures for removal of factory installed radios from 1975–82.

When removing the existing radio, use care. Don't cut wires—disconnect them at the connections. Remove the radio rear support bracket and reposition any trim pieces or air conditioner/heater ducts that may be in the way. You're going to need all the room you can find.

CAUTION: *Under no circumstances should you remove or disconnect any pressurized, air conditioning system hoses. Work of this type should be left to a qualified specialist.*

MAKE FINAL MEASUREMENTS

Now is the time to carefully check, recheck and check again all of the fit and installation measurements for the new equipment. Mark all areas to be cut or altered in any way before actually doing it. Constructing templates of cardboard or styrofoam frequently aid in determining final fits and installation positions.

Be sure that all of the installation hardware fits the radio and the vehicle dashboard.

RADIO/TAPE PLAYER INSTALLATION

There are basically three ways to mount your radio or tape player—in the dash, under the dash or in the console. In addition there are less popular ways, including transmission hump mounts, glove compartment mounts and under the seats. No matter which method you choose, be sure that:

1. The mounting position be as close to the horizontal as possible. Tape players, in par-

An under-dash mount (top) or transmission hung mount (bottom) are handy solutions to installation problems

In-Dash Installations

Temporarily install the radio into the mounting cavity. The shafts and nosepiece of the radio should fit through the holes and the nosepiece should butt against the rear of the dash without interfering with any of the radio controls. In this case, the nosepiece gasket can be used to take up any unwanted gaps in the installation.

If the shafts do not fit through the shaft openings in the dash, the shafts will have to be adjusted on the radio. Remove the radio from the mounting cavity and reposition the shafts on the chassis. Plan on a few trial fittings before you get the proper shaft spacing.

NOTE: *During trial fittings, try not to bump the ends of the shafts unnecessarily. Severe bumping of the shafts could damage the unit.*

If repositioning the shafts will not allow an interference-free fit, the only solution is to modify the dashboard. Normally, only slight modifications are necessary, but even these should be undertaken with great care. Mark the area to be modified and carefully file away a small amount of material at a time. Recheck the fit and repeat the process. The object is to remove the least material from the dashboard and use the face plate to cover any rough edges or small mistakes. You should wind up with the control shafts centered in the holes and the nosepiece of the radio roughly centered in the opening and abutting the rear of the dash.

In rare cases it will be necessary to cut brand new holes in the dash. This should be done only as a last resort and very carefully. Carefully mark the position on new holes by covering the area with masking tape and marking the position using the metal backing plate or faceplate from your new stereo as a template. Mark the size and location of the new holes in pencil on the masking tape. Make a starter hole with a center punch or an awl and carefully drill a hole in the center of the new hole area with the electric drill.

CAUTION: *Be sure there is nothing behind the area that will be damaged by the drill.*

Use a keyhole saw or coping saw to finish cutting the hole(s). Finish any rough edges

ticular, should be mounted a maximum of 30° from the horizontal.

2. The mounting is as solid and secure as you can make it. Again, with tape players, vibration transmitted through a less than secure mount will destroy the contact between tape and playback heads and upset tape speed accuracy.

3. The set does not block the flow of air or interfere with heater controls.

4. A power source and chassis ground are convenient to the set.

5. There is nothing behind the installation area that could be damaged during the installation process.

with a smooth file and remove the remaining masking tape.

NOTE: *An alternate method to cutting holes is with a hole cutting attachment used with the electric drill. These attachments are available in adjustable sizes and make a smooth, perfectly round hole.*

Once the nosepiece and shafts fit the dashboard openings, spacers can be installed over the control shafts, between the radio and rear of the dashboard to adjust the mounting position (depth) in the dash. Use sufficient spacers so that the shafts protrude the same distance and that the nosepiece fits flush with the nose gasket or face plate or protrudes a maximum of ¼". This may also take a few tries to get just the right spacing.

When you are satisfied that the installation of the chasis is as you desire, install the radio or tape player in the dash for the final time, with all spacers, gaskets, faceplates and trim plates. Install the washers and tighten the control shaft nuts.

NOTE: *Do not tighten the control shaft nuts too tightly. This can distort the position of the control shafts and cause the radio or player to malfunction.*

NOTE: *On tape players, do not forget to remove the tape player lockscrew, which is installed for shipment, to prevent damage to the tape transport. If the lockscrew is not removed prior to installation, the player will not function.*

Install the control knobs on the shafts and check for proper operation (on/off, freedom of operation, etc.)

Install a sturdy rear support brace on the radio. The brace is usually a long piece of

bendable metal (usually supplied with the radio), with a series of holes drilled in it, to adapt to almost any installation. Connect one end to the rear of the radio using the bolt supplied.

CAUTION: *Use of any other belt may damage the inside of the radio if it is too long.*

Connect the other end of the brace to a suitable mount under the dash. Use an existing belt or sheet metal screw if possible. If a hole must be drilled for a belt or screw, check behind the area for any components that could be damaged by a drill. Use the same procedure as you did for drilling a hole in the dash.

Under-Dash Installations

Under-dash installations are among the easiest to install and popular because of the wide variety of mounting locations. It is usually up to the owner, where to place the radio or tape player, but some thought should be given to possible locations.

1. Will the unit restrict the normal movement of the driver or passengers? Be sure that the unit will not interfere with the driver's operation of clutch or brake pedals.

2. Be sure that the unit is not installed more than 30° from the horizontal.

3. Be sure that the movement or operation of glove compartment doors, heater and air conditioner ducts or other accessories are not restricted.

4. Be sure the unit is placed so that all operating controls on the radio or player are convenient for normal operation.

5. Give some thought to the possibility of theft, since the unit will be in plain sight most of the time. One possible solution to this problem is to install a quick release bracket and connect the radio mounting hardware to the release bracket. Electrical and mechanical connections are made through a two-piece bracket, one of which mounts to the dashboard and the other to the radio or player, allowing quick and easy removal and storage.

The bracket that is supplied with a radio or player intended for under-dash mounting can be used as a template for marking the locations of holes (either in the dashboard or on the quick release bracket). Cover the area

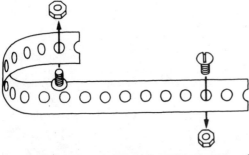

Use a metal support brace to anchor the rear of the radio

with masking tape and use a pencil to mark the location of holes to be drilled. Check on the other side of the area for any components that could possibly be damaged by the drill. Start the hole with a center punch or an awl and drill a hole. The size of the hole will be determined by the type of fastener to be used in fastening the bracket to the dash. If you will be using a nut/bolt combination, drill a hole just slightly larger than the outside diameter of the bolt threads and attach the radio mounting bracket to the quick release bracket using bolt, nut and lockwasher. If sheet metal screws are being used to attach the bracket to the dash, drill a hole the size of the root diameter of the sheet metal screw. It is also a good practice to use a lockwasher with sheet metal screws to prevent their working loose.

Once the unit is positioned, attach a rear brace to the radio and some other suitable location under the dash. Again, check to see what is on the other side before drilling holes to attach the rear support brace.

Other Mounting Locations

TRANSMISSION HUMP MOUNT

Attaching a radio or tape player to the transmission hump is really the same as the under-dash mount. The only difference is that the bracket is used upside down. Instead of hanging the radio or tape player from underneath the dash, it is now supported on top of the transmission hump or tunnel.

Before deciding on this mounting location, check under the car to be sure there are no hydraulic or fuel lines that are in the way of sheet metal screws. Be sure there is sufficient clearance between the floorpan and the transmission. Be sure there are no wires running under the carpet in that area that could be damaged during installation.

In particular be very careful not to damage any under car components in the drilling operation. It is very wise indeed to use a small, inexpensive plastic drill stop to be sure that the drill does not go too far past the floor pan. When drilling through a carpeted area, be sure to cut the carpet with a razor blade before trying to drill through the metal. If you

don't cut the carpet, the drill will unravel the carpet.

GLOVE COMPARTMENT INSTALLATIONS

Glove compartment installations are basically custom installations. Each one is different and presents its own special problems.

Before deciding on the glove compartment as the location for your car stereo, answer these questions.

1. Is there space for protruding tape cartridges?
2. Is a good ground source readily available?
3. Is a convenient power source readily available?
4. Can the unit be operated safely while driving?
5. Will a tape play with the glove box door closed?
6. Can a tape automatically eject with the glove box door closed?

GETTING POWER TO THE RADIO/TAPE PLAYER

This is generally a fairly simple operation. Car stereo systems are designed to operate on 12-volt, negative ground automobile electrical systems. It's easy to determine what type of system your car has, though normally it's not necessary. Cars manufactured after 1966 have 12 volt, negative ground systems. If you're not sure, count the filler caps on the battery. 12 volt batteries have 6 filler caps; 6-volt batteries have 3 filler caps. Next, find out which wire runs to the starter motor or starter relay. If it's the positive cable, the system is negative ground. If it's the negative cable the system is positive ground.

CAUTION: *If your car is either a 6 volt system or a positive ground system, consult your radio dealer. Special equipment will have to be used for the radio or tape player to operate.*

Car stereo manufacturers generally use red to indicate the "hot" wire, or wire that carries power to the unit. It is also the wire that holds the fuse. The easiest way to power your set is to crimp a spade type connector on the hot

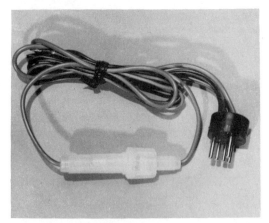

Most radios come with a power cord equipped with an in-line fuse holder

wire (after trimming it to the proper length) and plug it onto the terminal of the car's fuse box reserved for the radio operation. Using the fuse box terminals will let you use a power source that is switched ON and OFF with the ignition key, as opposed to having to turn the radio ON and OFF each time you get in or out of the vehicle. Some sets are equipped with a wire that must be connected to a power source that is "hot" all of the time. In cases such as this the clock terminal or wire, the cigarette terminal or wire or direct connection to the battery are good sources.

NOTE: *Tape players should be connected to a power source that is always "hot." This prevents shutting the ignition power OFF while a tape is in the unit, preventing flat spots on the tape player rollers.*

For 12-volt, negative ground systems, the battery positive (+) terminal provides the next best source of power, although it, too requires that the radio be manually switched on and off. The battery provides a stable power source for large power amplifiers and other units that require a large power drain.

A third source of power is the ignition switch or simply tapping into another hot wire such as the heater blower or cigarette lighter, or dome light. The ignition switch method is rarely used, since the advent of steering column mounted ignition switches and tapping into accessory wires can be a source of unwanted noise through the receiver.

Once you've decided on a power source, you'll have to install a suitable terminal on the other end of the hot wire. Trim the wire to the correct length, allowing it to be routed behind the dash in a position so that it will not run parallel to any other hot wires or run next to other motor driven components. The reason for this is to avoid unwanted static and noise from being picked up by the receiver's hot wire, a common source for interference to enter a stereo system.

It is important when installing terminal hardware that you get a solid connection, or noise will also enter the system at this point. Cut the wire to the routed length and leave a little slack. Use a pair of wire strippers to strip

Find a source of power (preferably at the fuse box) that will accept a spade connector

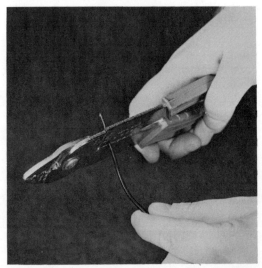

Strip about ½″ of insulation from the end of the wire

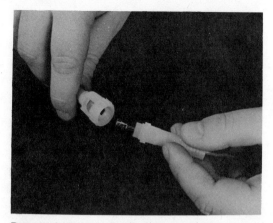

Be sure there is a 1.5 amp fuse installed in the hot wire

back about ½" of insulation from the end of the wire. Use the groove in the wire strippers corresponding to the gauge of the wire you're using. Twist the loose wire strands tightly together and insert them into the terminal hardware so that the insulation butts against the end of the hardware. Use pliers to crimp the ends of the terminal hardware over the bare wire ends. Trim the wire end that protrudes from the hardware and solder the connection, if desired.

Route the hot wire behind the dash and plug the spade connector onto the fuse box radio terminal. Be sure there is a 1.5 amp fuse installed in the in-line fuse holder.

RADIO/TAPE PLAYER GROUND WIRE

All receivers or tape players will also have a ground wire, in addition to a hot wire. The ground wire must be run to a suitable area on the vehicle that is attached to the chassis ground. Most of the metal areas on the vehicle will be grounded, but not all. Metal grounds on the firewall, structural points or the screws attaching the emergency brake release or parking brake pedal to the car are usually good grounds. Just remember that the unit will not operate unless the ground wire is connected to a grounded point on the vehicle.

Use the same procedures for connecting a terminal (use a flat U-shaped terminal or ring

lug instead of a spade connector) to the wire as in the preceding section dealing with the hot wire. Occasionally it will be necessary to drill a hole in the firewall and provide your own ground screw using a large sheet metal screw. Before drilling a hole, be sure to check on the other side for components that could be damaged by drilling. After drilling, sand the area thoroughly and use a star washer between the chassis ground and radio ground connection. Tighten it securely.

SPEAKER INSTALLATION

Location

By now, you should have decided on the location of your speakers. Other sections in Chapter 1 of this book go into the subject of speaker location more deeply and you should consult this section if you are still in doubt. Door or rear deck flush mounts will produce the best sound as (opposed to kick panel or dash mounts), so those are the ones we'll concentrate on. Procedures are essentially the same except that rear decks are not easily removed to work on.

Cutting Speaker Holes

Installing speakers in car doors is the most complicated installation, only because of the possibility of obstruction.

After deciding exactly where on the door panel to position the speakers, remove the door panel. It will be easier to cut the door panel if it is removed from the car door.

Before actually cutting any holes, carefully lay out the position of the speakers and check behind the area for any obstructions

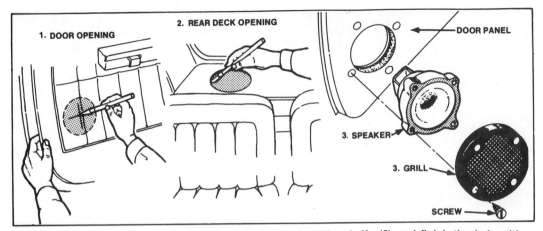

Mark the hole pattern with a template (1). Cut the fabric with a knife (2) and finish the hole with a saw or other cutter. Install the speaker and grille (3)

NOTE: *Door panels on GM products will require a special tool to remove the door window crank handles. The tool is available, inexpensively from most auto parts stores.*

Position the speaker and roll the window up and down and check for intereference between the speaker and door glass or operating mechanism. Check for the presence of wiring for electric door locks, power windows and similar equipment. Try to keep the speaker cover outside of the window crank area, but if that's impossible, be sure there is enough clearance between the window crank and the door panel to house the speaker grill cover.

Be sure that there is sufficient room behind the speaker for the magnet, so that it does not contact the outside skin of the door.

Mark the location of the speakers in the panel and follow the manufacturers instructions concerning the hole size. DO NOT HOLD THE SPEAKER UP TO THE PANEL AND TRACE AROUND IT! This will result in a hole large enough for the speaker to fall through and a ruined door panel. Use a piece of chalk to mark the hole. The chalk will easily wipe away when you're finished, yet can be seen against most surfaces.

Panels covered in leather, vinyl, carpet, or other similar materials should be cut with a razor blade first. Panels made of heavy cardboard, composition board, plastic or thin sheet metal can be cut with tin snips a key-hole saw or heavy shears, depending on the material. Use a large drill bit to drill a pilot hole for both door and rear deck speakers.

After cutting the hole in the panel, reinstall the panel on the door. Check to be sure of proper speaker fit. Any metal behind the panel can be marked for removal using the hole outline as a guide. Remove the panel again and file away the metal or remove it with a saw. File all the rough edges smooth and clean up loose metal filings, shavings and dust and other debris.

Insert the speaker in to the cut-out and mark the screw holes. Remove the speaker before drilling the screw-holes. Following the speaker manufacturers instructions, complete the installation of the speakers in the door panels or rear deck.

Speaker installed in panel, ready for speaker grille to be installed

Be sure to install any baffles or other sound enhancing pieces provided by the manufacturer

Connect the speaker wires to the speakers and label the wires before reinstalling the door panels.

Speaker Wiring

Wiring in general, and speaker wiring in particular is perhaps the most critical phase of any stereo installation.

Generally, it's best to choose the largest diameter wire possible. This will prevent heat build-up and make the system work that much easier. A high quality 16–18 gauge wire is generally chosen for speaker hook-ups. Solid core wire can be used, but braided wire is less susceptible to kinking and breaking.

To keep wires from suffering abuse, they should be routed under door sill plates, under carpeting or under a console, if possible. Periodically, you should wrap the wires around some stationary object to prevent terminals from tearing loose, if they are accidentally stressed.

The wires running to door speakers must inevitably run through the doors, and at this point, they should pass through rubber grommets or gobs of silicone sealer, if grommets are not available. Staggering the holes

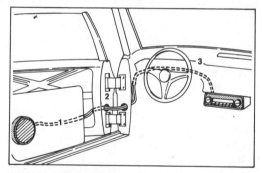

Wires to door speakers (1) can be run through holes in doors (2) and up under the dash (3)

by an inch or so will also prevent the wires from kinking as much as possible.

Wires should also be color coded at both ends for quick identification. If wire with multi-colored insulation is not available use colored marking pens as a substitute.

Use only the amount of speaker wire necessary to accomplish proper routing, and be sure to use the same length of wire on both channels. Speaker wire connection is very important to proper operation. Left and right speaker leads are usually coded green and grey respectively, and are normally connected to the white striped wires coming from

TROUBLESHOOTING

Radio problems are not normally caused by a defective radio. More often the cause is due to some less obvious fault. Follow the procedures in order before assuming the radio is defective.

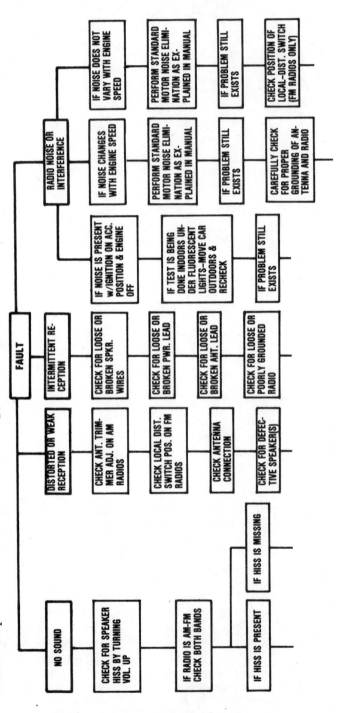

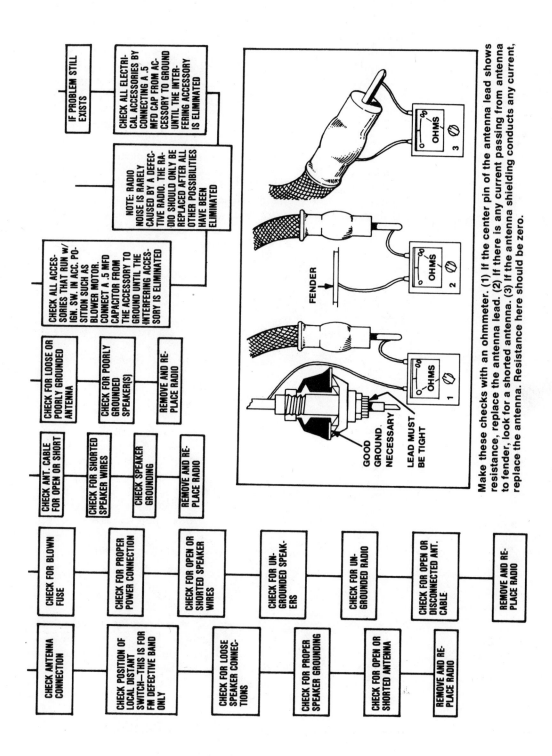

CHECK ANTENNA CONNECTION

CHECK FOR BLOWN FUSE

CHECK ANT. CABLE FOR OPEN OR SHORT

CHECK FOR LOOSE OR POORLY GROUNDED ANTENNA

CHECK ALL ACCESSORIES THAT RUN W/ IGN. SW. IN ACC. POSITION SUCH AS BLOWER MOTOR. CONNECT A .5 MFD CAPACITOR FROM THE ACCESSORY TO GROUND UNTIL THE INTERFERING ACCESSORY IS ELIMINATED

NOTE: RADIO NOISE IS RARELY CAUSED BY A DEFECTIVE RADIO. THE RADIO SHOULD ONLY BE REPLACED AFTER ALL OTHER POSSIBILITIES HAVE BEEN ELIMINATED

IF PROBLEM STILL EXISTS

CHECK ALL ELECTRICAL ACCESSORIES BY CONNECTING A .5 MFD CAP FROM ACCESSORY TO GROUND UNTIL THE INTERFERING ACCESSORY IS ELIMINATED

CHECK POSITION OF LOCAL DISTANT SWITCH—THIS IS FOR FM DEFECTIVE BAND ONLY

CHECK FOR PROPER POWER CONNECTION

CHECK FOR SHORTED SPEAKER WIRES

CHECK FOR POORLY GROUNDED SPEAKER(S)

CHECK FOR LOOSE SPEAKER CONNECTIONS

CHECK FOR OPEN OR SHORTED SPEAKER WIRES

CHECK SPEAKER GROUNDING

REMOVE AND REPLACE RADIO

CHECK FOR PROPER SPEAKER GROUNDING

CHECK FOR UNGROUNDED SPEAKERS

CHECK FOR OPEN OR SHORTED ANTENNA

CHECK FOR UNGROUNDED RADIO

REMOVE AND REPLACE RADIO

CHECK FOR OPEN OR DISCONNECTED ANT. CABLE

REMOVE AND REPLACE RADIO

GOOD GROUND NECESSARY

LEAD MUST BE TIGHT

FENDER

OHMS   1

OHMS   2

OHMS   3

Make these checks with an ohmmeter. (1) If the center pin of the antenna lead shows resistance, replace the antenna lead. (2) If there is any current passing from antenna to fender, look for a shorted antenna. (3) If the antenna shielding conducts any current, replace the antenna. Resistance here should be zero.

30 RADIO INSTALLATION

the speaker. The remaining wire is connected to the speaker ground wire from the radio. This is the normal method of connecting speakers, but some manufacturers recommend their own unique methods. Damage to the speakers can result if they are not connected properly, so follow the, directions carefully.

Each speaker has a positive and negative terminal and may be wired in series or parallel. Speakers wired in series connect the positive terminal of one speaker with the negative terminal of another speaker. Paral-

lel hook-ups use a positive terminal-to-positive terminal connection, and negative-to-negative. Wiring in series doubles the total impedance of the speaker pair, while parallel hook-up cuts the total impedance in half. The important factor here is the total impedance (load) on any given channel. The impedance rating on any given channel cannot exceed the impedance rating of the amplifier or you'll burn the system out. If you have any doubts, follow the manufacturers instructions or show the schematic to an expert.

Speakers must also be phased so that the audio signal can get through. To do this, simply make sure that the negative and positive speaker leads are hooked to the negative and positive terminals, respectively, on the amplifier.

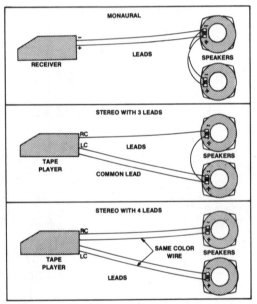

Use one of these examples to wire your speakers, depending on how many speaker leads exit from your radio/tape deck

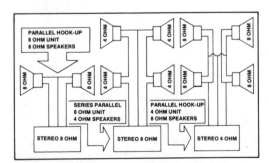

Learn the impedance rating of your stereo or tape player before wiring the speakers. These hook-ups accommodate multi-speaker installations

CHECK ALL CONNECTIONS

Before reconnecting the negative battery terminal, recheck and double check all of the connections to the set. Trace all of the wires backward from the receiver to the power source ground and speakers. Make sure everything agrees with the wiring diagram. Connect the antenna lead and reconnect the negative battery terminal. Be sure there is a fuse in the hot wire from the radio.

At this point an ohmmeter can be very helpful in determining the correct impedances between given points. Most do-it-yourself installers would be wise to consult a professional at this juncture.

Now is the time to put your installer's ability to the test and turn the system on.

MAINTENANCE

Car stereos require little maintenance. The mounting hardware for receivers and speakers should be tightened as necessary and speakers installed face-up should be kept free of debris.

Tape players on the other hand, require a comparatively high level of care. The playback and drive in the tape player accumulate a coating of tape residue as the tape passes over the playback heads. The residue should

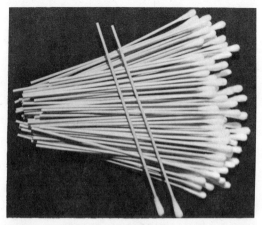

Cotton swabs are useful for cleaning tape player heads

Tapes should be stored in a clean, dry place, open end down

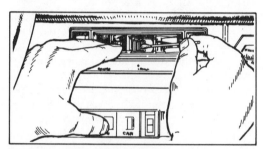

Clean the tape head and capstan every few hours of operation with a cotton swab and denatured alcohol

Use a tape demagnetizer cartridge to periodically demagnetize the playback heads

be removed periodically, by cleaning the heads with a cotton swab, moistened with alcohol. Hold the tape cartridge door open and swab the heads with the cotton swab. Do not use carbon tetrachloride and be sure to dry the surface with a dry swab.

Other things you should do to care for your tape player and cartridges are:

• Do not expose the cartridges to intense sunlight, heat or other temperature extremes. Tapes should be stored in a clean, dry place with the open end down to keep dust out of the cartridge.

• Do not attempt to open the cartridge or pull the tape from the cartridge.

• When the cartridge is not in use, remove it from the player. At the very least pull it out of the slot about an inch to prevent the rollers from flat-spotting.

• Do not shut off the power to the player while the unit is in operation.

3

CB RADIO AND ANTENNA INSTALLATION

Radio Shack CB equipment comes with owner's manual, set-up instructions, or installation procedures. Installation is not very hard. Follow the instructions and supplement them with some ideas here.

Some common hand tools are necessary see the Tools section of the preceding chapter: electric drill and bits, screwdriver, pliers, soldering gun and resin core solder, assorted wrenches, and wire strippers, etc. You will also need some wire end terminals and a few female spade-type connectors if you are going to go to the fuse block of your vehicle to power your mobile rig.

Radio Shack under-dash 40 channel CB radio

Radio Shack in-dash AM/FM Stereo/CB/Cassette player with CB controls built into microphone for convenient operation

INSTALLING MOBILE CBs

Mobile installations are not hard. The foremost problem is deciding where to put the set so that it will fit neatly, be relatively unobtrusive, be within easy reach, and be the least hassle to install. Each factor should be weighed before deciding on a place.

Radio Shack CB's do not present much of a problem because of their small size. Many could fit inside the glove compartment, except that they are hard for the driver to get at. The transceiver should be placed within easy reach of the driver so that operating the set is not distracting. The central engine cover on vans is a natural place, as is the below dash mount in passenger cars. Kits are also available for vans to provide a headliner installation, and one company offers an overhead console. These type installations have the advantage of the speaker facing downward and giving better sound. Other alternatives include transmission hump mount brackets, in-dash installations, or practically anywhere your imagination deems best.

Motorcycles usually mount the CB on the gas tank in a cradle supported on rubber dampers, as this is about the only possible place. RVs and tractor-trailers usually mount the radio on the lid of the dash console or on the windshield crossbeam preferred by 18-wheelers. Boaters normally mount the unit on the dashboard or on the dash gauge console.

The unit should fit neatly and unobtrusively, with emphasis on the unobtrusive. This is not to say that a careless installation is

CB quick disconnect mounts will discourage thieves

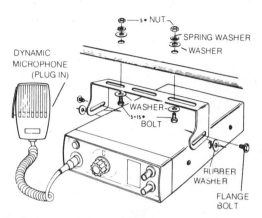

Typical under-dash installation

desirable, but CBs have become a popular item with thieves. Unless you plan to take your set with you or disconnect it every time you leave your vehicle, you had better give some thought to installing it where it will attract the least attention. Several other options are available here. there are CB lock mounts available to padlock your set to the car, but thieves are generally not too subtle about their work. Most times they will take the CB, lock mount and all, or worse take the whole car. A fairly good solution is to use the slide mounts popular with tape deck enthusiasts to mount your radio. This way you only have to disconnect the antenna lead-in and slide the unit off its mount to stow it in the glove compartment or under the seat. Another simple, but slower, solution to the problem is to use a two-pronged trailer harness to provide a quick-disconnect means for the power and ground leads to your set. After uncoupling the quick-disconnect, simply disconnect the antenna and the 2 or 4 screws holding the set to the bracket and stow the set out of sight and mind.

After spending many agonizing hours deciding where to put your new set, here's how to do it.

• Open the box and lay out all the pieces. Study the instructions and get a mental idea of just how the CB will be installed.

• After satisfying yourself that you have found the ideal mounting place, and you are sure it will fit there, attach the bracket to the radio and hold it up in position. Check that

the antenna cable can be easily connected or disconnected, and that the radio does not interfere with any heater or dash-mounted controls. Mark the position of the bracket on the sides or the forward edge.

If you have decided to use a slide mount for easy removal, you may or may not have to mount the normal bracket on the slide mount. It depends on what kind of set you have and what type of slide mount you have. In any case, follow the manufacturer's instructions for installing the slide mount. It is not really different from installing a normal mounting bracket, except that one piece attaches to the vehicle and one to the radio. Electrical contacts are provided so that when the slide mount is engaged, electrical contact is made.

• Take the bracket and set down, and remove the bracket. You're ready to mark and drill the bracket mounting holes. Put the bracket back in place and align it using the marks you just made. Mark the position of the center of the holes with a pencil dot. If you're afraid of scratching your custom paint job with the drill, lay down some small pieces of masking tape prior to marking the holes. Using a center punch and hammer, center-punch a small hole where the pencil mark is. This will prevent the drill from scratching surrounding metal as you drill the hole. Use a drill stop on your drill bit to avoid drilling through the mounting area when you don't know what's behind it. For most installations, use a drill which is the same diameter as the root diameter of the screw.

• Using the screws or the bolts and nuts

provided, securely fasten the mounting bracket in place. If you don't like the screws they gave you, get some you do like.

• Connect the microphone to the set, and hold the microphone at various places until you have found the best mounting spot. The mike hanger serves two purposes: (1) it keeps the installation neat and the mike out of the way when not in use; and, (2) if the microphone is allowed to hang from the set, it will stretch the cord and connections. Generally, you'll want to mount the mike in a convenient position where, eventually, you won't have to look to hang it up; you'll do it by feel. Likewise, you don't want it in a space where the cord is in the driver's way. You can screw the mike hanger to the dashboard using the same procedure for installing the bracket, or remove one of the screws from the radio housing and attach the hanger to the side of the set. If the idea of drilling more holes in your dash is repugnant, you can use a magnetic mike hanger.

• The next step is to determine battery polarity. You should have done this before you bought the set, but if you didn't, you're probably lucky (or prudent) enough to have bought a negative ground CB set. There are a few sets available which will work with negative or positive ground depending on how they're hooked up, but the vast majority are for 12 volt negative ground systems. If you are working with a 6 volt system, power inverters are available to convert 6 volts to 12 volts.

All modern cars use a 12 volt negative ground electrical system, although some heavy trucks are positive ground, and some older vehicles are 6 volt, positive ground. The battery polarity can be easily identified by seeing which battery terminal is connected to the chassis for ground. This is the ground side and the other side is the "hot" side or power source.

CAUTION: *Never, ever, hook a negative ground set to a positive ground or vice versa. Be sure to check polarity before hooking up a CB.*

• For most negative ground installations there are three popular sources of power, to which the fused lead on the CB set can be connected.

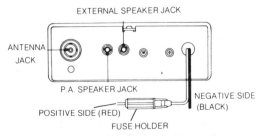

EXTERNAL SPEAKER JACK

ANTENNA JACK

P.A. SPEAKER JACK

POSITIVE SIDE (RED)

FUSE HOLDER

NEGATIVE SIDE (BLACK)

Typical connections at the rear of the set

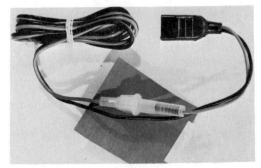

Most sets use a fused power harness with a plug at the set end

The best source is the positive, or the "hot," side of the battery. This is the best and most stable source of voltage, will lead to the least noise interference, and will provide power whether or not the ignition is "ON." A second source of power, and probably most popular, is the fuse block, usually located under the dashboard. Tapping the fuse block for power will provide a relatively stable voltage source and will enable your set to operate independently of the ignition switch, depending on which accessory terminal of the fuse block you tap. If this method is used, you will need to solder a female spade connector onto the end of the transceiver "hot" lead. A third, and least popular, way of getting power to the set is to use the accessory lead or terminal on the ignition switch, which will enable operation of the set only when the ignition switch is in the "ON" or "ACC" position. This method is rarely used since the advent of the steering column-mounted ignition switch.

Whichever method you select, be sure that you have the right polarity and be sure that the fuse clip (usually supplied with the set), is installed between the transceiver and the

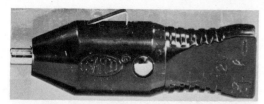

Cigarette lighter adaptors work fine as a power source

power source in the "hot" lead. The transceiver "hot" lead is generally fused with a 1.5 amp fuse, available at Radio Shack stores.

Cigarette lighters adaptor power cords work fine, too, but simply tapping other "hot" wires is not a recommended power source for best peformance, as they rarely provide a stable voltage source and can be the source of interference.

Once you've decided on a power source, you will have to install a suitable terminal on the end of the "hot" wire. For fuse box operation, install a female spade lug.

• It is important when installing terminal hardware on wire ends that you get a solid connection, or noise can enter the radio at this point. Cut the wire to length and leave a little slack. It's easiest to use a pair of wire strippers to strip about a ½ in. of insulation off the end. Use the groove in the strippers corresponding to the gauge wire you're using. Twist the loose wire strands together tightly and insert them into the lug so that the insulation butts against the barrel of the lug. Crimp the lug around the wire securely, using either the crimpers on the end of the pair of wire strippers or an ordinary pair of pliers. If you use pliers, try to get one side of the lug barrel to go under the other, making them overlap. When this is tightly crimped, finish the job by soldering the connection, after trimming the wire end which protrudes from the lug barrel.

If you're using a slide mount, the same procedures apply for wiring the stationary part of the slide mount as for wiring a CB. The only difference is that you'll have to follow the manufacturer's instructions for wiring the CB to the movable part of the slide mount. Strip a little bit of insulation away from the wire and solder it to the contacts. Make sure

that both parts of the mount are using the upper and lower sides of the same contacts, or you'll have no electrical contact.

• The "hot" lead is almost ready to be connected. Before going any further, cut the "hot" lead and install the fuse holder with fuse. After twisting the wire together in a "pigtail" connection, drop some solder on the pigtail and wrap it neatly with electrical tape.

• Decide where you are going to ground the transceiver. This can be almost anywhere—a screw or bolt which is nearby and electrically connected to the frame. If you can't find a screw nearby, drill a hole and use a sheet metal screw, in an out-of-the-way place (for neatness). Crimp and solder a ring or open-type lug onto the ground lead after cutting it to length. Use the same procedure as with the "hot" lead.

If your CB is not equipped with a plug on the rear of the set to disconnect the power and ground leads, you can do this easily. Most automotive stores sell 2-prong trailer connectors which only go together one way. They are inexpensive and solve the problem of disconnecting a ground lead from a bolt every time you want to remove your set from its mount. The 2-prong connector can be spliced into the power and ground leads easily, making sure that the circuits maintain their continuity. The connectors are generally color-coded to make this simple. Pigtail the wires together, apply a drop of solder, and securely tape the connection for a quick and easy disconnect.

• Turn the set "OFF" and route the leads. If it is necessary to route either of the leads through any sheet metal, drill an oversize hole and use a rubber grommet to prevent chafing. Stuff the leads out of the way and secure them with plastic ties salvaged from the kitchen. Connect the "hot" lead and the ground lead. When connecting the ground lead, scrape away a little paint to expose bare metal and use a toothed washer to get a solid ground. Tighten the grounding screw securely.

WARNING: *Do not, under any circumstances, operate the transceiver without connecting the antenna. You could blow out the output transistor.*

The installation of the set is complete; all that remains is to install the antenna.

INSTALLING MOBILE ANTENNAS

Before actually going out to get an antenna, look over your car, or truck and decide the best place for your antenna, for this will go a long way to determining what kind of antenna you get. The Radio Shack catalog has a mount for every purpose. If you have a car or pick-up truck, you can use just about any kind of antenna available—mirror mount co-phase, cowl mount, bumper mount, rooftop, or trunk lid mount. A base-loaded trunk lid mount is probably most popular with passenger cars because it requires no hole drilling in the body. In popularity, these are followed closely by 102 inch whips on bumper mounts and center loaded antennas on rain gutter mounts. More often than not, a van will have a base-loaded antenna installed on the roof to take advantage of the large metal surface area, affording a good ground plane. Pick-up trucks and tractor-trailer operators seem to favor the single or dual mirror mount, usually center-loaded. The reason is that the large expanse of metal on trucks will do a good job of blocking the radiated signal pattern and reflecting a good bit of it back into the antenna. The center-loaded antennas get the radiation pattern up in the air, away from sheet metal.

The basic consideration in antenna installation is height (as far as practicable and legal) but don't overlook the position of the antenna or the type, since both will influence performance to a great extent.

In general it is true that if your whip is not located in the center of the vehicle, the signal will be stronger in a direction diagonally across the vehicle from the antenna. If your antenna is mounted on the right front fender, the signal will be strongest toward the left rear fender. Give the placement of the antenna some consideration before deciding.

The possibilities for mounts and antennas are endless. They run from the simple gutter mount, to the popular trunk lid mount to the co-phased dual mount, known as "twin truckers." Some require hole drilling, some do not.

Swivel ball mount for flat surfaces

Trunk lip mount

Some can be equipped with quick-disconnect arrangements, others cannot. Naturally, two antennas are better than one, but be warned: they must be at least 78 inches apart to be directional. Some mounts will give better performance than others. You have to be very careful when mounting antennas on pick-up truck bodies or on West Coast-style mirror brackets. Either of these items can easily become electrically isolated from the chassis ground, resulting in an open circuit.

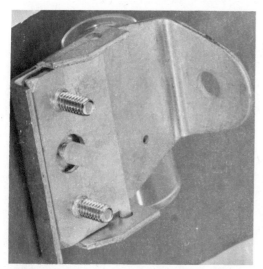

Gutter mount

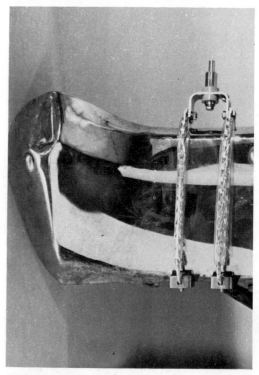

Bumper mount

Outside rear view mirror mount for "West Coast" mirrors

Likewise, you have to be careful locating magnetic mount antennas. SWR can and will vary significantly from one location to another. It's a good idea to mark the location on the car or truck where magnetic mounts were

Cowl mount

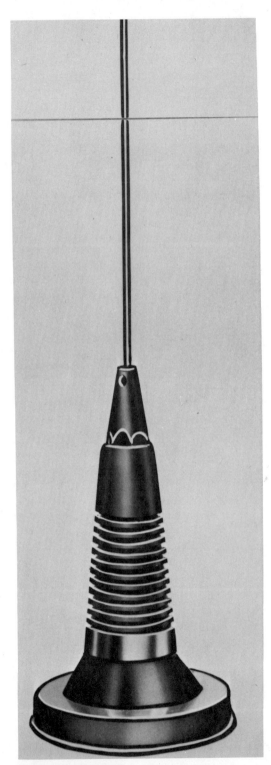

Magnetic roof mount

Base load antenna for trunk lip mount

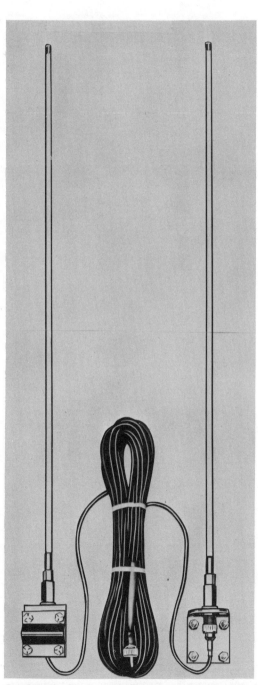

Continuous load, dual fiberglass antennas for mirror mount

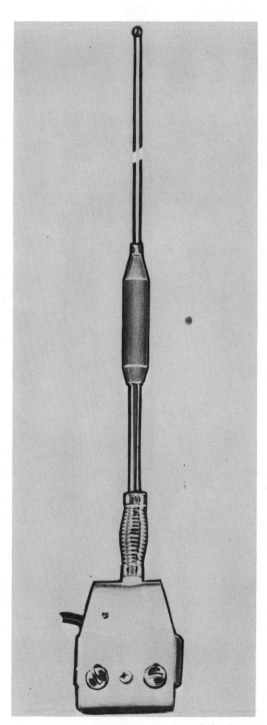

Rain gutter mounted center loaded antenna

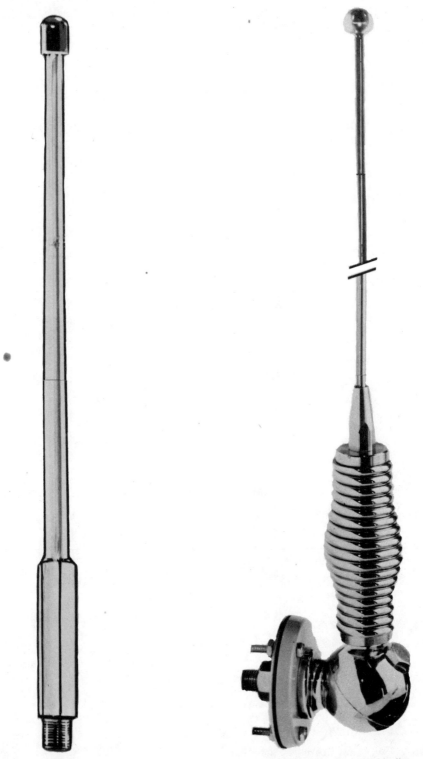

102″ fiberglass whip   102″ stainless steel whip on swivel ball mount

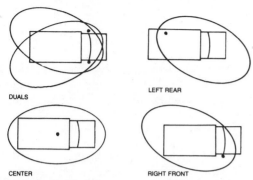

DUALS

LEFT REAR

CENTER

RIGHT FRONT

Effects of antenna location on range and direction. Effects vary with shape of vehicle

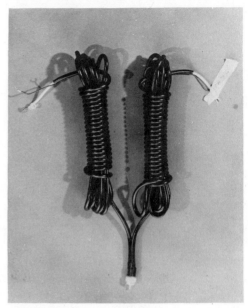

Co-phased (dual) antenna cable

tuned, so that they can be used in the same spot each time.

It's not an easy task to select an antenna; you'll probably agonize over it for hours, trying to balance off all the factors: maximum performance, location, type of antenna, cost, type of mount, length of cable, etc., etc. If at all possible, buy an antenna system, which is, one that comes packaged with the type of mount and antenna you want, the proper length of cable for the antenna, and the hardware. This will save having to buy the pieces separately. Also look for an antenna which has a resonator tip, tunable either by cutting it or by moving it up or down. This will save considerable time and effort.

• Once you have purchased the antenna system (or the antenna and the necessary hardware), lay out all the pieces and see how it goes together. If you bought your antenna system piecemeal, you're basically on your own, except for the recommendations made here which are common to all antennas.

• If you have a co-phased (dual) system, the place to start is at the transceiver by screwing the PL-259 connector into the set. All other installations should begin at the mount.

Do not shorten the coaxial cable supplied with dual antennas. Co-phase cable is RG-59/21 of 72 ohms impedance (net 50 ohm) and single whips use RG-58/21 of 50 ohm impedance. In all other installations, a general rule of thumb is to use the shortest cable possible, although it is not a wise idea to cut the length of the cable supplied with your antenna. It is usually around 18 feet long to accommodate

trunk lid mounts, and should be used as it is supplied.

• Install the antenna mount on the vehicle. If you are using a base-loaded antenna with a "no-hole" mount, it is relatively simple, as are bumper mounts. A ball mount or cowl mount will take a little more time. If it is necessary to drill a hole for the mount, drill a small pilot hole first and gradually enlarge the hole with several bits. From here the hole can be reamed to size (after applying a circle of masking tape around the hole to prevent paint chipping), or a metal hole saw can be used. Either way, file the edges of the hole when you're done to remove jagged edges.

• Connect the antenna cable to the antenna at the mount. Depending on the type of mount you're using, there are several ways of doing this. Most base-loaded antennas use a screw-on type mount. The outside insulation is stripped off to about 1 inch back, being careful to leave the coaxial shielding intact. Push the coaxial shield back and carefully remove the foam insulation from the center conductor. Slip the bare center conductor up through the hole in the mount and bend it over in the channel provided. Ground the coaxial shield as specified.

Ball mounts, mirror mounts, bumper

mounts and marine deck mounts, usually require that lugs be soldered onto the ends of the cable. Carefully cut away the outer insulation for about 2 inches, leaving the coaxial shield intact. Unbraid the coaxial shield and twist it together. Use the same procedure for attaching a lug of sufficient size, as was used to solder a lug onto the transceiver leads (also in this chapter). Cut away about ½ inch of the foam insulation from the center conductor and attach another lag to it in the same manner as before.

Connect the antenna and ground leads as suggested by the manufacturer. Clamp the wires in place to avoid chafing. Be sure to use all the insulation pieces supplied, and in the proper order of assembly.

• You are ready to route the cable. On trunk lid mounts the cable can be routed through the trunk (leaving enough slack to open the trunk), under the rear seat and along the driveshaft tunnel, coming up under the transceiver. It can also be routed along either side under the door sill threshold plate. Co-phased harnesses should be routed under the dash and through the body, using a grommet. Sometimes it is easier to route it through each door, since the mirrors are usually on the door. Be sure to leave enough slack in the cable to allow doors to open. For mirror mounts, run the cable along the mirror brackets and secure them with toothed plastic bundling ties. Connect them to the antenna mounts as previously described.

Cowl mounts usually require that the cable run through the firewall at some point. Try to route it away from the fuse box, electrical accessories, etc. Drill an oversize hole and use a grommet to prevent chafing.

Excess cable should be routed so that it is not in a tight loop. It should be in free, loose coils to prevent picking up interference.

• Install the antenna on the mount. At this point you can use any springs you might want, which should be installed now. Fiberglass antennas usually require a spring of some sort to prevent cracking when they hit low tree limbs, etc. Slip a piece of surgical tubing or vacuum hose over a long whip, where it could possibly chafe the body.

A quick disconnect is a good idea at this point, too. It will allow you to push down and turn the antenna to pick it off the mount any time you desire. Base-loaded antennas don't need this as they simply unscrew from the mount.

When you've finished the installation, check it against the following:

1. Don't put any unnecessary strain on the coaxial cable.

2. Avoid kinks and sharp bends.

3. Do not coil excess cable tightly; better to let it lie loose or under the floormats.

4. Keep the cable away from other wiring, especially ignition wiring.

5. Don't feed cable through hood hinges or other places where it could be damaged.

Tuning the Antenna

Now that everything is installed and the vehicle is back together, it only remains to tune the antenna. It must be tuned to obtain the lowest possible VSWR (variable standing wave ratio), which is a measure of how much radiated signal power is reflected back into the antenna. Most antennas are factory tuned for 1.5:1 or better, but VSWR of 1.1:1 is considered ideal, but seldom attained, and VSWR of 3:1 or more damage the transmitter.

Antennas are tuned in several ways:

A. Base-Loaded: These are usually equipped with an allen head set screw which is loosened to move the antenna shaft up or down. It may even require a little filing to shorten it.

B. Center-Loaded: These types usually have a resonator tip made of wire held in place by a set screw. They are also tuned by moving the resonator tip up or down or even shortening it slightly.

C. Continuous-Loaded: Continuous-load antennas are tuned either by loosening a thumbscrew and sliding a resonator tip up or down, or by removing the little cap from the antenna and filing a slight amount off the top.

D. Some antennas are tunned by sliding a small ball up or down the resonator.

Check the instructions before attempting to tune your antenna. You will need to buy an SWR meter, and maybe a 2 foot long patch cord equipped with a PL-259 on each end, or install a CB match box, to match antenna and transmitter.

Antennas should be tuned away from tall buildings, preferably in a wide open space, such as a parking lot on a day that the store's closed. Turn off the set and connect the SWR meter between the antenna and the transceiver; you will see an end marked "ANTENNA" and one marked "TRANSMITTER." The front of the meter has a switch, one side marked "FWD" (forward) and the other marked "REF" (reflected). Be sure that all doors and trunk lids are closed. Set the transceiver to Channel 1 and flip the switch to "FWD" and key the mike. The needle will jump. The SWR meter also has a "zero" knob. As you key the mike with the switch in FWD position, turn the "zero" knob until the needle aligns with the calibration line on the meter face. Let go of the mike switch and flip the meter to "REF." Key the mike again and read the SWR. Anything 1:1.5 or less is good and you need not go any farther. The other channels can be checked in the same manner. Just be sure you "zero" the meter each time you check. Don't key the mike for very long. A bad antenna mismatch can damage the rig.

The lower-numbered channels will generally read a slightly lower SWR than the higher-numbered channels. An ideal match would have Channel 12 (or 20) at 1:1 and channels 1 and 23 (or 40) at 1.5:1. The antenna is better slightly longer than too short.

If the SWR is above 1.5:1, you have to find out whether the antenna is too long or too short and act accordingly. If the SWR on Channel 1 is higher than on Channel 23 or (40), the antenna is too short. A quick way to tell is to grab the loading coil while reading SWR. If SWR goes down, lengthen the antenna, if it goes up shorten the antenna. Properly tuned antennas are very low SWR on the middle of the band and equal on channel 1 and 23 (or 40). If the SWR cannot be brought below 1.5:1, recheck the installation. You will find that most antennas are supplied proper length or overlength. Those antennas (fiberglass and steel whips), with no resonator tips can also be tuned by placing another lockwasher at the base to move it up slightly, or, if necessary, an antenna matchbox can be used.

If it is determined that the antenna is too long and must be cut, do it judiciously, for it is possible to go too far. Cut, file, or grind in about $1/16$–$1/8$ inch increments, checking the SWR at Channel 1 and 23 (or 40) each time until you are satisfied. Always cut the antenna at the bottom of the resonator. The little ball at the top is a static discharge ball and should not be cut off. When you are through the resonator tip should be fully inserted into the loading coil and the set screw tightened securely. Twin antennas must be trimmed IDENTICALLY.

Troubleshooting the Antenna

What if the antenna and nature conspire against you and all attempts to reduce the dreaded SWR end in failure? Turn off the rig and disconnect the antenna. Borrow an ohmmeter or run down to your local CB shop. Check the resistance between the inner conductor and the shell on the antenna connector (cable side). A completely open or shorted circuit could be the result of a kinked, cut or otherwise damaged cable. Be sure that none of the fine wires in the coaxial braid are shorting to the center conductor. Any suspicious connectors should be cut off and reconnected or replaced.

Check the mount for resistance between the antenna and ground; check for shorts; and check for an open circuit between the antenna and the point at which the inner conductor is connected.

If all else fails, install a matchbox at the transceiver end of the coax. This can be adjusted for minimum SWR.

NOISE SUPPRESSION

NOTE: *Although noise suppression is more closely identified with CB radios, the procedures will work equally well with AM/FM noise problems.*

Noise, or interference, is classified as one of two types—RFI or TVI. RFI (radio frequency interference), is interference with the ability of your CB set to receive signals and is commonly known as static. TVI (television interference), is generated by your CB set and will sometimes affect the TV, radio, or hi-fi radio reception in close proximity to your

TROUBLESHOOTING CB ANTENNA PROBLEMS

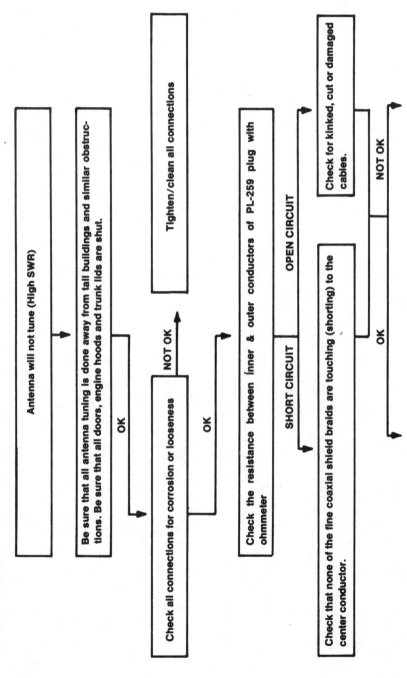

Antenna will not tune (High SWR)

Be sure that all antenna tuning is done away from tall buildings and similar obstructions. Be sure that all doors, engine hoods and trunk lids are shut.

OK

Check all connections for corrosion or looseness

NOT OK → Tighten/clean all connections

OK

Check the resistance between inner & outer conductors of PL-259 plug with ohmmeter

SHORT CIRCUIT

OPEN CIRCUIT

Check for kinked, cut or damaged cables.

NOT OK

OK

Check that none of the fine coaxial shield braids are touching (shorting) to the center conductor.

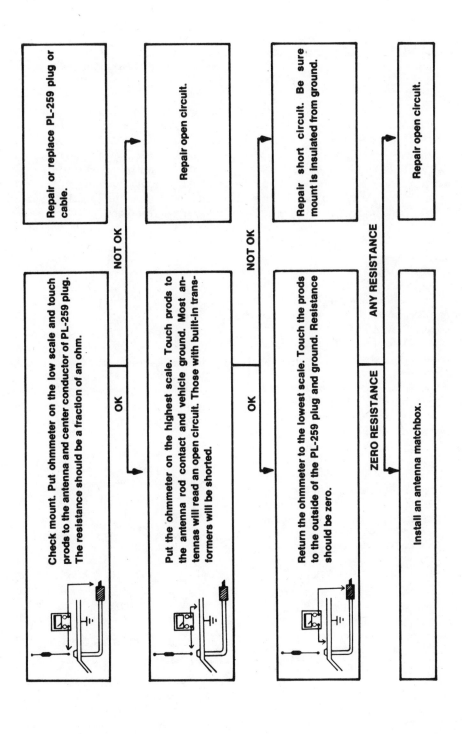

Check mount. Put ohmmeter on the low scale and touch prods to the antenna and center conductor of PL-259 plug. The resistance should be a fraction of an ohm.

OK

NOT OK

Repair or replace PL-259 plug or cable.

Put the ohmmeter on the highest scale. Touch prods to the antenna rod contact and vehicle ground. Most antennas will read an open circuit. Those with built-in transformers will be shorted.

OK

NOT OK

Repair open circuit.

Return the ohmmeter to the lowest scale. Touch the prods to the outside of the PL-259 plug and ground. Resistance should be zero.

ZERO RESISTANCE

ANY RESISTANCE

Repair short circuit. Be sure mount is insulated from ground.

Install an antenna matchbox.

Repair open circuit.

transmitter. Both are annoying depending on whether you're listening to your CB or your neighbors are trying to use their TV or hi-fi. The degree of noise suppression needed will vary in each different case. Each case is unique, requiring its own solution.

RFI Noise

RFI noise falls into two classes, either man-made or natural. Natural noise, atmospheric disturbances, sunspots, lightning, etc., are a problem with CB, but little can be done about controlling them. Man-made noises produced by electric motors, vehicle electrical systems, farm machinery, medical equipment, and machinery of all types, are the main cause of noise, and, fortunately, you can do something about these.

Because of the low power used for CB, its phenomenal growth in the last few years, high receiver sensitivities, and the proximity to sources of interference, the RFI problem can be severe even though almost all CBs employ noise limiters. Vehicles built in the United States are provided at the factory with adequate suppression for reception on AM/FM receivers which conforms to SAE suppression standards, but CB, and all other types of two-way communication equipment, requires the same basic suppression techniques, but far more extensively and carefully.

In cars, trucks, and RVs, noise can get into the transceiver in one or more of three ways: through the power source, through the antenna, or picked up by the internal circuitry of the receiver. Don't confuse background noise with interference. Concern yourself with it only if it disrupts reception at normal volume.

There are two fundamental approaches used to suppress noise: reduce the strength of the interference at the source; or, to confine the interference, using the engine compartment as a shielding box. Capacitors, bonding, routing of wiring, and high-voltage suppressors are the basic hardware and techniques used.

CAPACITORS

A capacitor is designed to pass the flow of alternating current, but to block the flow of di-

CONVENTIONAL BYPASS CAPACITOR

COAXIAL CAPACITOR

Two types of capacitors (Courtesy Champion Spark Plug Co.)

rect current. Interference of this type (man-made), is almost always an alternating or impulse type of signal and the capacitor will direct most of the flow of this type of current to ground without affecting the circuit of the direct current. A conventional by-pass capacitor is suitable for the broadcast band, but for effective suppression with higher UHF frequencies, the use of coaxial capacitors is recommended.

CAUTION: *Capacitors should never be used on transistorized or electronic ignitions.*

BONDING

Bonding is a particular technique used to connect the metal parts of the vehicle together to form an effective shield blocking RFI. Interference generated by the ignition and charging systems will be kept from traveling throughout the vehicle and a common ground will be formed for all RFI signals.

WIRE ROUTING

Wire routing must be carefully done; if not, interference will be transferred from one circuit to another, particularly to the high voltage, or ignition cable side.

HIGH-VOLTAGE SUPPRESSORS

The ignition system is probably the greatest single source of RFI in a vehicle, and resistors are available to reduce the interference to a tolerable level.

General Suppression Procedures

Anytime two-way radio or audio equipment is replaced or serviced, the following steps will help minimize the need for additional suppression.

NOTE: *Before attempting any of the procedures outlined in this section, disconnect*

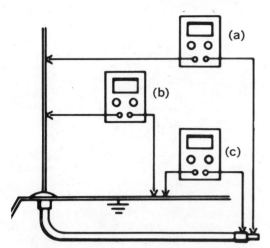

3 checks you can make on your antenna with an ohmmeter (Courtesy Champion Spark Plug Co.)

the wires from the battery. If you don't, you could be seriously injured.

1. Be sure that all of the original equipment for suppression is still intact and in good condition. It's possible that resistor cable could have been replaced by non-resistor cables, a bonding strap could have been removed, or a toothed lockwasher may have been lost.

2. Be sure that all components and connections are in good condition. A corroded connection will, in all likelihood, make interference worse.

3. Tune the engine or have it tuned by a specialist. Tune-up should include new spark plugs, points, and condenser at the least. Additional items which should be looked at, but require replacement less frequently, are the cap and rotor. Optimum radio performance will not be delivered unless the ignition system is in good condition.

4. Ideally, the radio should be connected to the battery. Connecting it to the accessory or ignition side of the ignition switch leads to interference in the radio from the car's electrical system.

5. Low-voltage wires should be kept away from the ignition system, as well as any other circuits which are suspected noise producers. Wires of suspected circuits should be laid flat against a grounded metal area where possible; they should not be bundled together.

6. Be sure that the antenna lead-in shield is grounded at both ends. Insulation, as well

as all connections, should be clean and tight.

If you possess an ohmmeter, there are three checks you can make on the antenna. If you don't own an ohmmeter, try to borrow one to make these three checks.

a. Put the ohmmeter on the lowest scale and touch the prods to the antenna rod and to the center contact of the plug. The resistance should be a fraction of an ohm;

b. Put the ohmmeter on the highest scale. Touch the ohmmeter prods to the antenna rod and to the vehicle ground. Most antennas should read an open circuit, except for the few high "gain" type antennas with built-in transformers, which will be short-circuited;

c. Return the ohmmeter to the lowest scale. Touch the prods to the outside of the antenna plug and to the vehicle ground. Resistance should be zero.

If any of these tests don't turn out as they should, there is a serious fault or open circuit in the antenna system.

7. Above all, good suppression can only take place if all components are properly connected and grounded. All paint, oil, grease, or rust should be removed from all areas where good electrical contact is essential. Clean hardware and sharp-toothed washers should be used for mounting components. All places where lugs or eyes have been attached should be soldered to the wire, and all electrical connections should be taped.

If, after you have done all this and the evil noises still persist, you will have to conduct a step-by-step search to identify the culprit.

Identifying Interference

Each type of interference you hear on the receiver has its own distinctive sound and characteristics. In order to find out what is causing the interference, you at least have to know where to start looking.

IGNITION SYSTEM: This is a popping sound which increases in tempo with the engine speed. It will also shut off immediately when the ignition key is turned off at fast idle.

GENERATOR/ALTERNATOR: These produce a musical whine, high-pitched, increasing in frequency with higher engine speed. It will not shut off instantly when the ignition key is turned off at fast idle.

VOLTAGE REGULATOR: Voltage regulator interference is usually heard in conjunction with alternator or generator noise, and makes its appearance as a rasping, ragged sound occurring at an irregular rate. It will not stop instantly when the ignition is shut off at fast idle.

INSTRUMENTS: Instruments in the dash produce hissing, crackling, and clicking sounds occurring at irregular intervals as the gauges operate. The condition is usually worse on rough roads and can be tested by jarring the dashboard.

The voltage limiter behind the dash, which is used with the fuel and temperature gauges, can produce a loud "hashing" sound at intermittent intervals. Bouncing the vehicle to activate the fuel gauge sending unit should verify RFI from the voltage limiter.

Disconnect the gauges or the sending units one at a time; the RFI should disappear if they are at fault.

ACCESSORIES: Make a preliminary check with all accessories turned off. Turn them on one at a time and listen for increased RFI. Intermittent noise from the turn signal or hazard warning flashers or windshield wipers can often be eliminated by the use of a capacitor, but most by-pass capacitors will have no effect on wiper motor noise. Coaxial capacitors should be used for this.

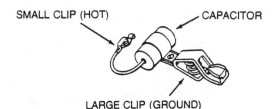

Using a grounded capacitor to identify the source of interference by the process of elimination (Courtesy Champion Spark Plug Co.)

WHEELS & TIRES: Wheels and tires sometimes create a popping or rushing sound through radio while they operate on dry roads at high-speeds. Interference from the wheels and tires can be traced by lightly applying the brakes; the noise should disappear.

OTHER SOURCES: If a particular type of interference cannot be identified as coming from any of the sources described above, a test capacitor can be easily constructed as shown. A grounded capacitor touched to all "hot" electrical connections will identify the offending item if the RFI disappears.

Another test instrument can be constructed at home which is very useful in locating the source of RFI. Begin by disconnecting the antenna from the receiver. Wrap 50 turns of insulated, or bell, wire into a coil 2 inches in diameter, and tape the coil of wire to a broom stick or wooden dowel rod as shown. Using a few feet of normal lamp cord, connect one side of the coil to an alligator clip which will be used for the ground side. The other end of the coil should be connected to the center conductor of a PL-259 connector which can be purchased from any electronics or CB store. Basically, what you have done is to construct a crude inductive antenna which will pick up interference. Connect the PL-259 to your radio, start the engine, and turn the radio on. Probe around the engine and wiring with your homemade coil. Interference will be the loudest when you are close to the source of the interference.

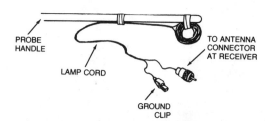

Home-made antenna for locating the source of interference by probing (Courtesy Champion Spark Plug Co.)

RFI Suppression Techniques

CAUTION: *Capacitors should not be used on transistorized or electronic ignitions.*

ALTERNATOR

The alternator slip-rings should be clean and the brushes should make good contact. A 0.5 mfd (microfarad), coaxial capacitor can be installed at the alternator output terminal. Be sure that it is rated to handle the alternator output current.

NOTE: *Do not connect a capacitor to the alternator field terminal.*

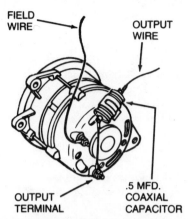

Capacitor installed at the alternator output terminal (Courtesy Champion Spark Plug Co.)

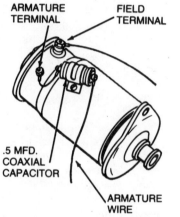

Capacitor installed at the generator output terminal (Courtesy Champion Spark Plug Co.)

GENERATOR

Most American (or import), cars and trucks these days are not equipped with generators. But, for the cars which are, the commutator and brushed should be making good contact. If the commutator is badly worn, the generator should be overhauled.

Remove the factor-installed capacitor from the armature terminal and install a 0.5 mfd coaxial capacitor which is rated to handle the current output of the generator.

NOTE: *Do not connect the capacitor to the generator field terminal.*

VOLTAGE REGULATOR

Many of the newer cars are now using solid state regulators, often built into the alterna-

tor. But, for those cars still equipped with the traditional external voltage regulator of the single or double-contact type, a 0.5 mfd capacitor can be installed as close as possible to the *armature* and *battery* terminals. On a single contact regulator, use a 0.5 mfd capacitor at the ignition terminal. Again, be sure that the capacitor(s) are rated to handle the generator or alternator current output. The rated output can be found in the electrical specifications of most any service manual for your car.

Capacitors should not be connected to the regulator *field* terminal. Unusual cases of interference may require that the FIELD wire be shielded. In this case, be sure that both ends of the shield are grounded.

If regulator noise is extreme or simply cannot be quieted, the wire from the "F" or field terminal can be replaced with a piece of RG-8/U coaxial cable. If you do this, be sure that the coaxial cable does not touch the engine block or any other accessory delivering a lot of heat. Also, be sure that the braid at the ends of the coaxial cable is securely grounded to the chassis or nearest ground point other than the engine.

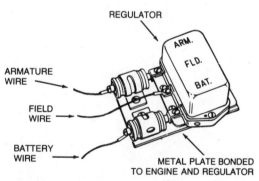

Capacitors installed at the regulator "Arm" and "Bat" terminals.

INSTRUMENTS

A 0.5 mfd capacitor installed at the terminals of the gauges or sending units will usually silence interference from these sources.

The voltage limiter can usually be quieted with a 0.5 mfd capacitor connected at the battery terminal of the voltage limiter. In place of this, a 0.1 mfd radio-type pigtail capacitor connected across the voltage limiter terminals also will work. Extreme cases of noise

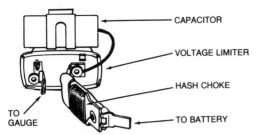

Hash choke installed in series at voltage limiter (Courtesy Champion Spark Plug Co.)

from the voltage limiter can be cured by installing a "hash choke" in series with the battery lead.

ACCESSORIES

Almost any accessory which is operated by a brush motor (turn signals, stop signals, electric windows, heater blowers, and the like), can be quieted with a 0.25 mfd capacitor installed at the accessory terminals.

BONDING

Bonding straps can be pieces of ½–1 inch wide copper braided strap for connecting components to ground, or pieces of metal for

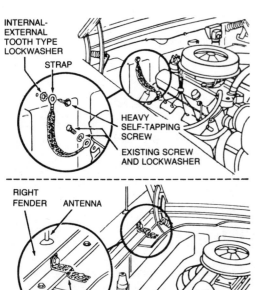

Examples of bonding (Courtesy Champion Spark Plug Co.)

grounding fenders. Braided copper straps can be obtained from most well-stocked electronic supply stores. In addition, many car manufacturers and radio manufacturers offer bonding kits of this material. If you can't find the copper stuff, an alternative is to use the braided coaxial shielding from a piece of spare coaxial antenna cable. You can get this off by carefully slitting the outside insulation from the coaxial cable (without slitting the shielding). Peel away the insulation and slip the braided shielding off the foam insulation. Whatever type of bonding material is used, be sure that the lugs used to attach the cable are securely attached to the cable and soldered.

The art of "bonding" is largely a matter of luck and trial-and-error. The location of the bonding straps often plays an important role in its effectiveness, and experience will most times reveal the best location. An expert at CB installations can offer words of wisdom on this subject.

Some good places to begin installing bond straps are:

Corners of the engine to the frame;
Exhaust pipe to the frame and engine;
Both sides of the trunk and hood lids;
Coil and distributor-to-engine and firewall;
Air cleaner-to-engine;
Battery ground-to-frame;
Tailpipe-to-frame;
Steering column, oil pressure gauge line and any other metal lines passing through the firewall;
Front and rear bumper supports; and
Radiator-to-radiator supports.

Generally, any metal parts which are separated from the frame by any type of insulation (spacers, paint, noise silencing material), should be electrically connected to the frame, or connected together.

Use self-tapping screws in conjunction with toothed lockwashers to cut into surface layers of metal. Bonding straps should be as short and heavy as possible to be really effective, and should be checked periodically for corrosion and tightness.

WHEELS

Static collector rings, installed inside the front wheel caps, will collect static build-up from the front wheels and prevent it from entering the receiver.

Primary Ignition System
IGNITION COIL

The first step is to remove the ignition coil and its mounting bracket. Clean the paint from the back of the bracket with sandpaper or a file and from the mounting point on the engine. Reassemble the bracket and the ignition coil tightly.

If this does not help, install a 0.1 mfd coaxial capacitor as close to the coil battery terminal as possible. Do not connect the coaxial capacitor to the distributor terminal, nor should a normal by-pass capacitor be used. In addition, a 0.005 mfd 1,000 volt ceramic disc capacitor installed at the coil distributor terminal will help eliminate interference.

Be sure to check coil polarity, or have it checked.

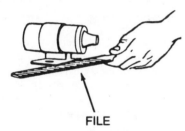

FILE

Clean the back of the coil mounting bracket (Courtesy Champion Spark Plug Co.)

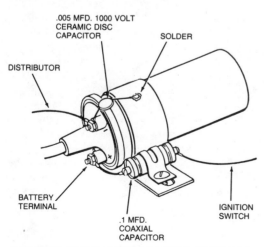

.005 MFD. 1000 VOLT CERAMIC DISC CAPACITOR   SOLDER

DISTRIBUTOR

BATTERY TERMINAL

.1 MFD. COAXIAL CAPACITOR

IGNITION SWITCH

Capacitors installed on the ignition coil (Courtesy Champion Spark Plug Co.)

DISTRIBUTOR BREAKER POINTS

The distributor breaker points are not usually the cause of interference, although they cannot be totally ignored as a cause of RFI. Point condition determines to a large extent whether or not they will produce any interference. Points which have been well-maintained are far less likely to cause any interference problems than are those which have been poorly maintained. If the points are suspected of causing a great deal of interference, look for point bounce or deteriorated points.

Fleets and commercial trucks can reduce RFI and at the same time increase point life by determining the allowable condenser limits for the vehicle, and selecting condensers at the high limit for mainly stop/start driving or selecting condensers at the low limit for mainly high-speed driving. If the condenser limits are determined to be 0.18–0.25 mfd, use a 0.25 mfd condenser for stop/start driving or a 0.18 mfd condenser for high-speed use.

NOTE: *By-pass capacitors should not be installed at the coil distributor terminal.*

DISTRIBUTOR CAP AND ROTOR

The distributor cap and rotor should be replaced at the interval specified by the vehicle manufacturer. In terms of suppressing RFI,

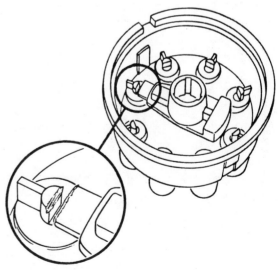

Replace rotor and distributor cap (on point-type ignitions) when they show signs of wear (Courtesy Champion Spark Plug Co.)

they should be replaced when the tip of the rotor and the contacts in the cap show signs of erosion or carbon tracking, which increases the gap over which the spark must jump, leading to higher RFI levels.

The rotor used with a GM V-8 distributor can be had in a radio suppression version, which is stamped with an "E" on the metal blade.

Secondary Ignition System

This is the high-voltage side of the ignition system and the worst producer of RFI. Radiated interference is reduced effectively by suppressor resistors of various types. Some are separate components, while others have been incorporated into the distributor rotor or spark plug towers on the cap. These are mainly service items for U.S. cars and trucks.

SPARK PLUG CABLES

SAE standards specify two resistance ranges for cable use on newly-manufactured vehicles:

LR—3,000-7,000 ohms per foot;
HR—6,000-12,000 ohms per foot.

Of the two, LR is the most common, but HR is sometimes used between the coil and distributor where short cables are involved.

Replacement wires of the resistance type are available from any of several manufacturers. The resistance data is generally available on the box or from the manufacturer.

Wen handling suppressor cables, never pull on the cable; remove them by pulling on the boot. Never try to attach a screw-on suppressor to a suppressor cable and don't try to repair suppressor cables. Cables which are damaged should be replaced.

RESISTOR SPARK PLUGS

Spark plugs of the type known as "resistor type" afford better protection from RFI than conventional spark plugs. The use of resistor-type spark plugs is increasing in newer engines because of their ability to maintain their suppressive characteristic for long periods of time.

Spark plugs should also be maintained properly to provide protection against RFI. A wide plug gap, when the electrodes are burnt, or uneven, requires higher than normal voltage causing the ignition system to emit higher than normal levels of RFI.

COMBINING SUPPRESSION DEVICES

Some cars and trucks are equipped with resistor-type plugs and suppressor spark plug cables. Resistor-type plugs can be used in other vehicles where more suppression is desired, or some other suppression devices can be used, but combining the two is not a good idea. Choose between:

Resistor plugs with suppressor cables,
OR
Resistor plugs with 10,000 ohm suppressors in the center tower of the distributor and 5,000 ohm suppressors in the spark plug distributor towers.

SAFETY WARNING DEVICES

Federal safety regulations have required the addition of a variety of warning lights and buzzers over the past few years. These buzzers are to remind the driver to turn the headlights off, fasten seatbelts, remove the ignition key, etc. If necessary, these circuits can be suppressed at the primary power circuits.

Be careful when hooking up your transceiver to a power source—it is not a good idea to connect it to any source shared with a buzzer, solenoid, or flasher.

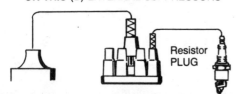

THIS (A) SUPPRESSOR TYPE CABLE

Resistor PLUG

OR THIS (B) EXTERNAL SUPPRESSORS

Resistor PLUG

Do not combine spark plug suppression devices (Courtesy Champion Spark Plug Co.)

4

OEM RADIO
REMOVAL

The following procedures cover the removal of radios supplied as original equipment by the car or truck manufacturer preparatory to installing a replacement unit. Only those radios supplied as original equipment by the vehicle manufacturer are covered in this section.

The procedures are those that appear in Chilton's 1982 Auto Repair Manual and cover 1975–82 vehicles.

Installation of replacement radios is covered in Chapter 2 of this book. Also refer to the installation instructions packed with the radio.

NOTE: *In every instance, without exception, no factory installed radio should be removed or any substitute radio installed without first disconnecting the negative battery terminal. Battery terminal should be reconnected only after reinstallation is completed and all connections are checked for accuracy.*

The following precautions should be observed when working on a car radio:

1. Always observe the proper polarity of the power connections; ie., positive (+) goes to the power source and negative (−) to ground (negative ground electrical system).

2. Never run the radio without a speaker; damage to the output transistors will result. If a replacement (or additional) speaker is used, be sure that it is of the correct impedance (ohms) for the radio. The proper impedance is stamped on the case of American Motors radios.

3. If a new antenna or antenna cable is used, adjust the antenna trimmer for the best reception of a weak AM station around 1400kc; the trimmer is located behind or above the tuning knob or in the radio case near the antenna lead. On tape player radios, it is in the cartridge slot.

4. For best FM reception, the best antenna height is 31–33 in.; for best AM reception, the antenna should be at its full length.

54   OEM RADIO REMOVAL

DOMESTIC CARS

Apollo ... 57
Aries ... 68
Aspen ... 67
Astre ... 78

Belair ... 64
Bobcat ... 69
Bonneville (1975–81) ... 79
Bonneville (1982) ... 77

Cadillac ... 59
Calais ... 00
Camaro ... 61, 62
Capri ... 73
Caprice ... 64
Catalina ... 79
Cavalier ... 63
Century (Rear Dive) ... 57, 58
Century (Front Drive) ... 58
Celebrity ... 64
Charger ... 68
Chevelle ... 61
Chevette ... 64
Chrysler ... 67
Ciera ... 77
Cimarron ... 61
Citation ... 62
Comet ... 71
Concord ... 56
Continental ... 73
Cordoba ... 67
Coronet ... 68
Corvette ... 64, 65
Cougar ... 70, 73
Cutlass ... 75, 76

Dart ... 67
Delta 88 ... 75
DeVille ... 59
Diplomat ... 67

Eagle ... 56
Eagle SX-4 ... 56
Eldorado ... 60, 61
Electra ... 56
Elite ... 70
Escort ... 69
EXP ... 69

Fairmont ... 73
Firebird ... 79
Fleetwood ... 59
Ford ... 71
Formula ... 00
Fury ... 68
Futura ... 73

Granada ... 73
Gran Fury ... 67, 68
Grand AM ... 78
Grand Le Mans ... 78
Grand Prix ... 79
Grand Ville ... 79
Gremlin ... 56

Horizon ... 68
Hornet ... 56

Impala ... 64
Imperial ... 67

LeBaron (1975–81) ... 67
LeBaron (1982) ... 69
LeMans ... 77
LeSabre ... 56
Lincoln Mark IV, V, VI, Town Car . 74, 75
Lincoln Continental ... 74
LN-7 ... 69
LTD & LTD II ... 70
Lynx ... 69

Magnum XE ... 68
Malibu ... 61
Mark IV, V, VI ... 74, 75
Marquis ... 71
Matador ... 56
Maverick ... 71
Mirada ... 67
Monaco ... 68
Monarch ... 73
Monte Carlo ... 61
Montego ... 70
Monza ... 66, 67
Mustang ... 73
Mustang II ... 69

Newport ... 67
New Yorker (1975–81) ... 67
New Yorker (1982) ... 67
Nova ... 61

Omega (thru 1979) 77
Omega (1980 and later) 77
Omni 68

Pacer 56
Phoenix (Front Drive) 78
Phoenix (Rear Drive) 77
Pinto 69

Regal 58
Reliant 68
Riviera 56
Royal Monaco 68

Seville 60, 61
Skyhawk 58
Skylark (Front Drive) 58
Skylark (Rear Drive) 57
Spirit 56
St. Regis 67
Starfire 76
Sunbird 78

Thunderbird 70, 71, 73
Torino 70
Toronado 75
T1000 77

Valiant 67
Vega 66
Ventura 77
Versailles 73
Volare 67

XR-7 (Cougar) 73

Zephyr 73

88 75
98 75
400 69
2000 80
6000 80

IMPORT CARS

Audi 89
BMW 80
Capri 81
Colt/Challenger (Dodge) 81
Datsun 81
Fiat 83
Fiesta (Ford) 83
Honda 84
Mazda 84
Mercedes-Benz 85
MG 87
Isuzu (Opel) 87
Opel 87
Porsche 87
Peugeot 89
Arrow/Champ/Sapporo (Plymouth) 89
Subaru 89
Toyota 89
Triumph 91
Volkswagen 91
Volvo 92

TRUCKS AND VANS

Chevrolet 92
Chevrolet LUV 93
Datsun 93
Dodge 94
Ford 95
Ford Courier 92
GMC 92
International Harvester 96
Isuzu 98
Jeep 98
Mazda 98
Mitsubishi 95
Plymouth 94
Toyota 98
Volkswagen 99

AMC

Matador

1. Disconnect the negative battery cable. Remove the knobs from the radio and unfasten the control shafts retaining nuts.
2. Remove the bezel securing screws, and remove the bezel.
3. Loosen, but do not remove, the upper radio securing screw.
4. Raise the rear of the radio to separate its bracket from the upper securing screw.
5. Pull the radio forward slightly, and disconnect all of the leads from it. Remove the radio.

Hornet, Gremlin, Concord, Spirit, and Eagle

1. Disconnect the battery ground cable.
2. On Gremlins and Hornets through 1977, remove the package tray and the ash tray and bracket.
3. Pull off the radio knobs and remove shaft retaining nuts.
4. Remove the bezel retaining screws and remove the bezel. On 1978 and later models with A/C, remove the center housing of the instrument panel.
5. Disconnect the speaker, antenna, and power leads, and remove the radio.

Pacer

1. Disconnect the negative battery cable.
2. Remove the radio knobs, attaching nuts, cluster bezel, and overlay cover.
3. Loosen the radio-to-instrument panel attaching screw.
4. Lift the rear of the radio and pull forward slightly. Disconnect the electrical connections and the antenna and remove the radio.

BUICK

Electra, LeSabre, Riviera Through 1976

1. Remove the knobs and escutcheons from the radio. If equipped with Trip-Set and/or Speed-Alert, remove the cone-shaped knobs.
2. Remove the face plate by pulling outward. Disconnect the terminal connector before completely removing the face plate, if equipped with Trip-Set/Speed-Alert.
3. Remove the two hex nuts from the control shafts.
4. Remove the ash tray and frame.
5. Disconnect the two connectors behind the dash and unplug the antenna.
6. Unscrew the support bracket nuts and remove the radio to the rear and downward.

Electra, LeSabre, Riviera—1977 and Later Without Air Bags

NOTE: *On 1981–82 models except Riviera remove the headlight switch and place the gear shift lever in the low position to remove the left hand instrument panel.*
1. Disconnect the battery ground cable.
NOTE: *On 1981 and later Rivieras remove the center trim plate by grasping it firmly and pulling out. Be careful not to lose the spring retaining clips.*
2. Remove the ashtray and bracket.
3. Pull off the radio knobs and trim washers.
4. Remove the lower left air duct.
5. Remove the two retaining nuts from the control shafts.
6. Unplug the power lead, speaker wire, and antenna lead.
7. Remove the rear radio mounting nut.

Electra, LeSabre, Riviera— 1975–76 With Air Bags

1. Turn the ignition lock to the LOCK position.
2. Disconnect the battery ground cable and tape its end thoroughly to prevent any possibility of a short circuit.
3. Remove both lower instrument panel cover trim plates after prying them out.
4. Disconnect the parking brake release cable and remove the lower left instrument panel cover assembly by removing the 8 retaining screws.
5. Remove:
   a. 2 horizontal screws below the instrument panel.

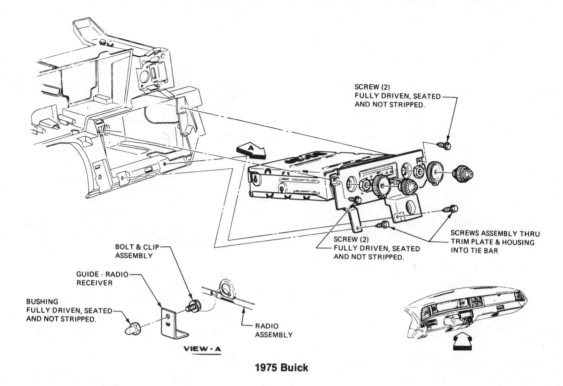

SCREW (2)
FULLY DRIVEN, SEATED
AND NOT STRIPPED.

SCREWS ASSEMBLY THRU
TRIM PLATE & HOUSING
INTO TIE BAR

BOLT & CLIP
ASSEMBLY

GUIDE · RADIO
RECEIVER

BUSHING
FULLY DRIVEN, SEATED
AND NOT STRIPPED.

RADIO
ASSEMBLY

SCREW (2)
FULLY DRIVEN, SEATED
AND NOT STRIPPED.

VIEW · A

1975 Buick

b. 4 vertical screws on the upper horizontal instrument panel surface.

c. 2 screws from the outside of the glove box door hinge.

d. 1 screw from the right-side of the instrument panel cover.

6. Disconnect the radio, speakers, convector (remote unit) connectors, and antenna lead cable from the radio.

7. Release the 4 clips behind the instrument panel by grasping the tongue of the far right-side clip, squeezing, and pulling forward.

8. Remove the radio knobs and escutcheons from the shafts.

9. Carefully pull the trim plate off the instrument panel housing.

10. Remove the retaining nuts from the shaft.

11. Unscrew and remove the power antenna relay.

12. Loosen the nut on the left radio support. Remove the right support nut.

13. Lower the radio from beneath the instrument panel.

14. If the car has a radio/tape unit, remove

the two convector (remote unit) mounting screws and remove the convector from the right-side of the instrument panel housing support.

Century/Regal Through 1977

1. Remove the radio knobs.

2. Disconnect the center air duct assembly control, if so equipped, by removing the two retaining screws.

3. Disconnect the left side air conditioning hose, if so equipped.

4. Disconnect the radio wiring.

5. Loosen the radio supporting nut.

6. Remove the two front attaching nuts at the radio face and slide the radio toward the front of the car.

Apollo and Skylark Through 1979

1. Disconnect the negative batter

2. Remove the radio kn

and the side brace s

3. Disconnect the radio wiring and the antenna lead.

4. Remove the radio from under the dash.

Century 1978–81, 1978–82 Regal

1. Disconnect the negative battery cable and remove the radio knobs.

2. Remove the center trim plate.

3. Remove the glove box to gain access to the radio.

4. Disconnect the radio mounting bracket.

5. Disconnect the radio wiring.

6. Remove the radio with the bracket attached.

1975 Skyhawk

1. Disconnect the battery; remove the clock knob and trim panel.

2. Remove the instrument panel cover, glove compartment, and four attaching nuts from above the glove compartment door.

3. Lower the steering column by removing the nuts holding the column to the upper bracket guide.

CAUTION: *Be extremely careful not to let the column drop or hang unsupported.*

4. Disconnect the speedometer cable from the speedometer; remove the instrument cluster assembly.

5. Remove all the knobs and escutcheons from the radio; remove the radio support bracket retaining screw from the lower dash.

6. Disconnect the electrical connections and antenna lead wire, remove the radio.

Skyhawk—1976–80

1. Disconnect the battery negative cable ~~~ull off the radio control knobs and

~~~ deep well socket, remove the ~~~ and washers.

~~~enna wire, and remove ~~~he radio to the in-

~~~ mounts at-

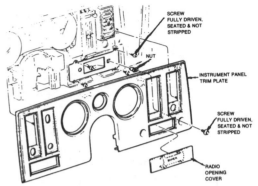

1980–82 Skylark instrument panel removal

Skylark—1980–82

1. Disconnect the negative battery cable.

2. Remove the center instrument panel trim plate.

3. Remove the radio attaching screws and pull the radio out to gain access to the wiring. You may have to remove the ashtray retainer assembly to gain access to the radio wiring.

4. Disconnect the wiring. Remove the knobs and separate the face plate from the radio.

Skyhawk—1982

See Chevrolet Cavalier

Century—1982

1. Disconnect the negative battery cable.

2. Remove the instrument panel trim plate.

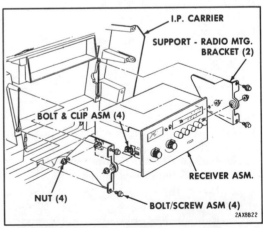

1982 Century

3. Remove the right side instrument panel switch trim by removing the 3 screws and gently rocking the panel out.

4. Remove the radio mounting screws.

5. Unplug the antenna and disconnect the electrical leads.

6. Remove the radio through the front of the instrument panel.

CADILLAC

Full Size Cadillac Without Air Bags (A.C.R.S.)—1975–76

1. Remove the 4 screws each which secure the lower steering column cover to its reinforcement and the instrument panel support.

2. Take the lower cover off.

3. Unfasten the screws which secure the lower ash tray bracket, and then remove the two screws from the left-hand ash tray bracket.

4. Unfasten the right-hand ash tray securing screw. Remove the ash tray assembly from the dash panel.

5. Remove the knobs, washers, outer rings, and shaft retaining nuts.

6. Remove the radio-to-dash panel lower support brace nut from the back of the radio.

7. Loosen, but don't remove, the screw which secures the brace to the support, and turn the brace clockwise.

8. Slide the radio back from the instrument panel. Detach the speaker connector, power connector, and antenna lead from it.

9. Turn the dial side of the radio (front) so that it is facing down, and lower the left-side of the receiver. REmove it through the ash tray opening.

Full Size Cadillac With Air Bags (A.C.R.S.)—1975–76

1. Turn the ignition switch to Lock.

2. Remove the negative battery cable and tape its terminal end.

CAUTION: *If the battery cable is not disconnected and taped, there is a chance that the air bag could accidentally deploy.*

3. Remove the 3 screws which retain the glovebox in the dash, but don't remove the two striker screws.

4. Remove the glovebox partition screws,

and set the glovebox aside, without disconnecting the wiring.

5. Remove the tape storage compartment retaining screws and remove the compartment.

6. Remove the ash tray assembly retaining screws, pull the assembly out part way, unfasten the electrical leads, and remove the assembly.

7. Remove the knee restraint left trim screw.

8. Remove the screws, and loosen, but don't remove, the fifth screw (under the steering column) from the bottom of the knee restraint.

9. Remove the 4 knee restraint securing screws working from the tape storage compartment and ash tray openings.

10. Perform Steps 5–7 of the radio removal procedure for 1975 and later Cadillacs without air bags.

11. Through the knee restraint opening, disconnect the antenna lead, depress the locktabs and push the electrical connections upward to disengage them.

12. Clear the instrument panel support by turning the radio to the left. Slide the radio away from you, lower the front of the radio (dial), and remove it, front first, through the knee restraint opening.

Except Seville—1977–80

1. Remove the radio knobs and anti-rattle springs. Disconnect the negative battery terminal.

2. Remove the two hex nuts securing the bezel to the radio.

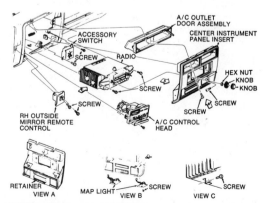

1977 and later except Seville

3. Remove the two center air conditioning outlet grilles. Remove the one screw in each outlet.

4. Remove the maplights and remove the center panel insert.

5. Unbolt and remove the radio from the panel.

6. Disconnect the wring.

All Except Seville—1981–82

1. Remove the center instrument panel insert and appliqué.

2. Remove the screws holding the radio to the lower instrument panel.

3. Disconnect the antenna and electrical connectors and remove the radio.

Seville—1976–78

1. Disconnect the negative battery ground.

2. Loosen the right forward screw which secures the fuel injection electronic control unit cover to the unit.

3. Remove the remaining three screws from the cover.

4. Remove the three screws which secure the unit to the panel supports.

5. Carefully lower the control unit enough to disconnect the three electrical connectors

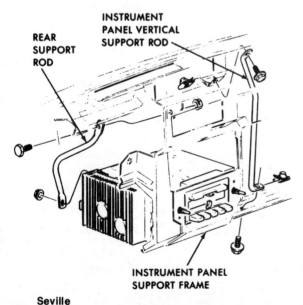

REAR SUPPORT ROD

INSTRUMENT PANEL VERTICAL SUPPORT ROD

INSTRUMENT PANEL SUPPORT FRAME

Seville

from the left hand side and the hose from the front of the unit. Remove the unit.

6. Remove the screw securing the climate control outlet extension to the heater case.

7. Disconnect the antenna.

8. Remove the radio support rod.

9. Remove the control knobs, anti-rattle springs, control rings and both hex nuts.

NOTE: *The control knobs on radios with 8-track are retained with $5/64$ in. allen screws.*

10. Remove the radio.

Eldorado Through 1976

Refer to the Cadillac Section for radio removal and installation procedures for these years.

Eldorado—1977–78

1. Remove the four screws attaching the steering column cover to the reinforcement.

2. Remove the four screws attaching the cover to the instrument panel cross support.

3. Remove the ash tray lower bracket screw.

4. Remove the two screws from the left side ash tray mounting bracket.

5. Working from the lower edge of the instrument panel, remove the ash tray right side attaching screw.

6. Remove the ash tray. Disconnect the bulb and the electrical connector.

7. Remove the radio knobs, the anti-rattle spring, the control rings and the retaining nuts.

8. Remove the brace nut at the rear of the radio.

9. Loosen the brace supporting screw and rotate the brace to the right.

10. Slide the radio from the instrument panel and disconnect the wiring.

11. Rotate the dial side downward and remove the radio through the ash tray opening.

Eldorado and Seville—1979–81

1. Disconnect the negative battery cable.

2. Remove the two phillips head screws

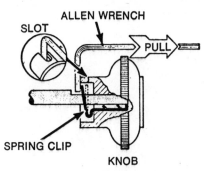

Radio knob removal

from the top of the instrument panel center insert.

3. Remove the radio knobs and remove the insert.

4. Remove the rear window defogger switch to gain access to the left side mounting screw.

5. Remove the mounting screw.

6. Remove the radio and disconnect the wiring.

Cimarron

Refer to the Chevrolet Cavalier section for radio removal.

Eldorado and Seville—1982

1. Remove the center instrument panel insert and applique.

2. Remove the mounting screws.

3. Pull the radio rearward and disconnect all electrical connectors.

4. Disconnect the antenna and remove the radio.

Cimarron

1. Remove the instrument panel trim piece.

2. Unbolt the upper radio bracket from the instrument panel.

3. Disconnect all wires and antenna and remove the radio.

4. Disconnect the bracket from the radio.

CHEVROLET

Chevelle and Monte Carlo— 1975–77

1. Disconnect the battery ground cable.

2. Remove the left air conditioner lap cooler duct.

3. Pull off the knobs and bezels.

4. Remove the control shaft nuts and washers. You will probably need a deep well socket.

5. Remove the support bracket stud nut. Disconnect the antenna, speaker, and power wires.

6. Move the radio back until the shafts clear the instrument panel. Lower it from behind the panel.

Malibu and Monte Carlo—1978 and Later

1. Disconnect the battery ground.

2. Pull the control knobs from the shafts.

3. Remove the trim plate.

4. Remove the wiring and antenna cable from the rear of the radio.

5. Remove the receiver stud nut at the right side bracket.

6. Remove the control knob nuts.

7. Remove the instrument panel bracket.

8. Remove the radio through the panel opening.

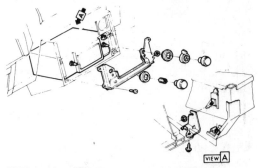

1978 and later Malibu and Monte Carlo

Nova and Camaro (thru 1981)

1. Disconnect the battery ground cable.

2. Pull off the knobs and bezels.

3. Remove the control shaft nuts and washers. A deep well socket will be needed

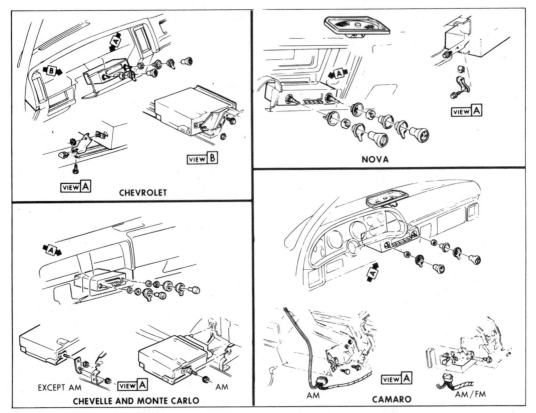

VIEW B

VIEW A

CHEVROLET

NOVA

VIEW A

EXCEPT AM   VIEW A   AM

CHEVELLE AND MONTE CARLO

AM   VIEW A   CAMARO   AM/FM

1975–76 Chevrolet and 1975–77 Nova, Chevelle and Monte Carlo

on the Camaro. Remove the Camaro center air duct and hose, if present.

4. Remove the mounting bracket screws or nuts.

5. Move the radio back until the shafts clear the instrument panel. Lower it and disconnect the antenna, speaker, and power wires.

Camaro 1982

1. Disconnect the battery ground cable.

2. Remove the 3 screws securing the console bezel.

3. Remove the 4 screws attaching the radio to the console.

4. Remove the radio from the console and disconnect the electrical connectors and antenna lead.

Citation

1. Disconnect the negative battery cable.

2. Remove the radio knobs, the shaft nuts, and the clock knobs, if equipped.

3. Remove the instrument cluster trim bezel attaching screws and pull the bezel rearward.

4. Remove the headlamp shaft and knob. Reach behind the instrument panel bezel with a long screwdriver and push the headlamp shaft release button to release the knob.

5. Disconnect the wiring and remove the bezel.

6. Remove the two screws attaching the radio bracket to the instrument panel.

7. Pull the radio rearward while at the same time twisting it slightly to the left, and disconnect the electrical connectors and antenna lead. Remove the lamp socket.

8. Remove the radio.

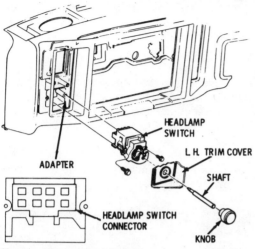

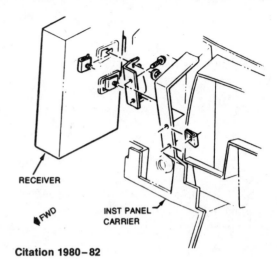

Citation 1980 – 82

The headlamp switch is removed on all models by pulling the knob out, depressing the retaining button on the switch assembly, removing the knob and shaft, and removing the switch

Cavalier

1. Disconnect the negative battery cable.
2. Remove the instrument panel trim plate by removing the six torx screws attaching the trim plate to the instrument panel.

3. Check the right side of the radio to determine whether a nut or stud is used for side retention. If a nut is used, remove the hush panel, and loosen the nut from below on non-A/C cars. On A/C cars, remove the hush panel, A/C duct, and A/C control head for access to the nut. Loosen the nut enough to pull the radio out. Do not remove the nut. If a rubber stud is used, go on to next step.

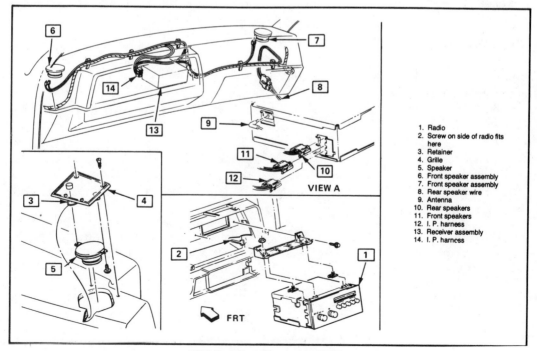

1. Radio
2. Screw on side of radio fits here
3. Retainer
4. Grille
5. Speaker
6. Front speaker assembly
7. Front speaker assembly
8. Rear speaker wire
9. Antenna
10. Rear speakers
11. Front speakers
12. I. P. harness
13. Receiver assembly
14. I. P. harness

VIEW A

FRT

1982 Cavalier, Cimarron, J2000

4. Remove the two radio bracket-to-instrument panel attaching screws, then pull the radio forward far enough to disconnect the wiring and antenna. Remove the radio.

Celebrity

1. Disconnect the battery ground cable.
2. Remove the instrument panel trim plate.
3. Remove the 3 screws at the radio bracket.
4. Pull the radio rearward and disconnect the electrical connectors and antenna.
5. Remove the radio.

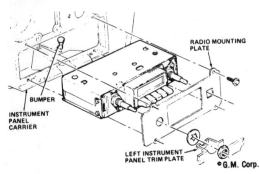

1982 Celebrity

Chevette

1. Disconnect the negative battery cable.
2. Remove the nut from the mounting stud on the bottom of the radio.
3. Remove all control knobs and/or spacers from the right and left radio control shafts.

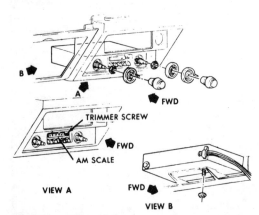

Chevette—All models

4. Remove the four screws from the center trim plate and pull the trim plate and the radio forward slightly.
5. Disconnect the antenna lead from the rear of the radio.
6. Disconnect the speaker and electrical connectors from the radio harness.
7. Disconnect the electrical connectors from the rear window defogger and cigarette lighter.
8. Use a deep well socket to remove the retaining nuts from both control shafts and remove the radio.

Bel Air, Caprice, Impala—1975–76

1. Disconnect the negative battery terminal.
2. On cars with A/C, remove the lap cooler duct.
3. Turn the radio control knobs until the slots in the bottom of the knobs are visible. Depress the metal retainers with a screwdriver and remove the knobs and bezels.
4. Remove the control shaft nuts and washers.
5. Remove the right side bracket-to-instrument panel bolt and the stud nut on the left side of the radio.
6. Pull the radio forward and disconnect the wiring from the radio and remove the radio from the car.

Bel Air, Caprice, Impala—1977–82

1. Disconnect the negative battery terminal.
2. Pull the knobs off.
3. Remove the three screws and the trim plate.
4. Remove the two screws and the bottom nut holding the radio to the instrument panel.
5. Detach the wiring and the antenna.
6. Remove the radio and the mounting bracket.

Corvette—1975–77

1. Disconnect the negative battery cable and remove the right instrument panel pad.

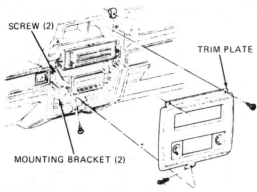

1977 Chevrolet

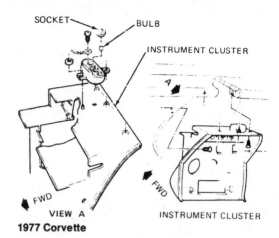

1977 Corvette

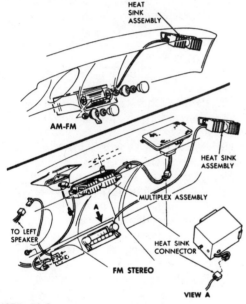

1975–76 Corvette

2. Disconnect the radio speaker connectors.

3. Remove the wiper switch trim plate screws and tip the plate forward to gain access to the switch connector. Remove the switch connector and trim plate from the dash.

4. Unclip and remove the right and left forward console trim pads. Remove the forwardmost screw on the left and right sides of the console.

5. Working with a flexible drive socket between the console and the metal horseshoe brace, remove the nuts from the studs on the lower edge of the console cluster.

6. Remove the remaining console attaching screws and disconnect the radio electrical connectors, antenna wire and radio brace from the rear of the console. Remove the radio knobs and nuts.

7. Pull the top of the console rearward and separate the radio from the console and remove it from the right side opening.

NOTE: *The center instrument cluster trim panel is designed to collapse under impact. Do not deflect the panel to gain access to the radio.*

NOTE: *The radio heat sink must be removed when radio service is required. It is located behind the passenger side dash panel.*

Corvette—1978–82

1. Disconnect the battery ground cable.

2. Remove the console tunnel side panels.

3. Pull the radio control knobs from the shaft.

4. Remove the two screws that secure the console trim plate to the instrument cluster.

5. Remove the rear defogger switch if so equipped.

6. Remove the five screws from around the upper perimeter of the instrument cluster.

7. Pull the instrument cluster enough to disconnect the electrical connector from the rear of the cluster.

NOTE: *The center instrument cluster trim panel is designed to collapse under impact.*

Do not deflect the panel to gain access to the radio.

8. Remove the screw holding the radio bracket reinforcement to the floor pan.

9. Pull the radio outward and disconnect the wiring from the back.

10. If a new radio is being installed, save the mounting bracket from the rear of the old one.

NOTE: *The radio heat sink must be removed when radio service is required. It is located behind the passenger side dash panel.*

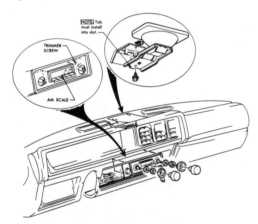

Vega—typical of all models

Vega

1. Remove the battery ground cable.

2. Remove the knobs, controls, washers and nuts from the radio bushings.

3. Disconnect the antenna lead, power connector, and speaker connectors from the rear of the receiver.

4. Remove the two screws securing the radio mounting bracket to the instrument panel lower reinforcement and lift out the radio receiver.

Monza—1975

1. Disconnect the battery ground cable.

2. Remove the clock set stem knob and instrument panel bezel.

3. Remove the glove compartment.

4. Remove the radio knobs and nuts.

5. Remove the instrument panel pad.

6. Remove the lower screws from the radio mounting bracket.

7. On air conditioned cars, remove the left cap cooler and duct.

8. Remove the steering column mounting bracket and lower and support the steering column.

9. Remove the 3 screws from the top of the instrument cluster.

10. Remove the 3 bolts from the reinforcement on the instrument panel carrier.

11. Disconnect the speedometer drive cable from the speedometer head.

12. Pull the instrument panel slightly forward and disconnect the electrical and antenna leads.

13. Remove the radio from the instrument panel.

14. Installation is the reverse.

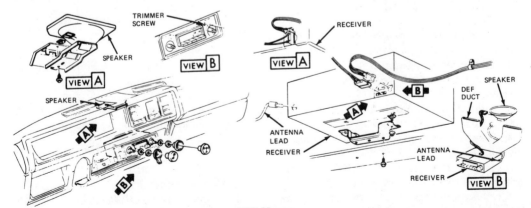

1975 Monza

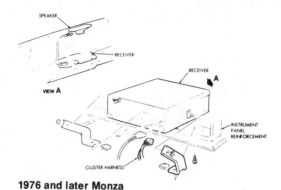

1976 and later Monza

Monza—1976 and Later

1. Disconnect the negative battery cable.
2. Remove the knobs, bezels, nuts, and washers from the radio control shafts.
3. Remove the two screws attaching the radio to the instrument panel reinforcement.
4. With mounts still attached, lower the radio and disconnect the electrical leads.

CHRYSLER CORPORATION (CHRYSLER, DODGE AND PLYMOUTH)

Valiant, Dart

NOTE: *If the car is equipped with air conditioning, it will be necessary to remove the two air outlet assembly-to-instrument panel mounting nuts from the underside of the panel and drop the assembly down and remove it from under the instrument panel. It will also be necessary to remove the ash tray and ash tray housing.*

1. Disconnect battery.
2. From under panel, disconnect speaker, antenna, and wiring leads at radio.
3. Pull off the knobs and remove the shaft nuts.
4. Remove two radio mounting nuts from panel and remove radio to lower support bracket mounting screw. Hold radio in position and remove radio bracket.
5. Move radio toward the front of the car, down, and out from under instrument panel.

Volare, Aspen, Diplomat, LeBaron, Mirada, 1981–82 Imperial, 1980–82 Cordoba, 1982 New Yorker, and Gran Fury

1. Disconnect the battery ground cable. On the Aspen, Volare, Diplomat, LeBaron, and 1982 New Yorker and Gran Fury remove the instrument cluster bezel by removing the four screws along the lower edge, placing the automatic transmission selector in 1, and pulling out to detach the top edge clips. Remove center bezel on Mirada, 1980–82, Cordoba, 1981–82 Imperial.
2. Remove the radio mounting screws.
3. Pull the radio from the panel and disconnect the wiring and antenna.
4. Remove the radio.

Chrysler and Imperial—1975–78

1. Disconnect the battery ground cable.
2. Remove the instrument cluster bezel.
3. On monaural radios, remove the lamp assembly from the front of the radio.
4. Remove the radio to panel screws.
5. Remove the instrument panel upper cover. Work through the access hole in the top of the instrument panel to disconnect the antenna and speaker leads. Remove the bracket mounting nut.
6. Remove the radio and detach the electrical lead.

Chrysler Newport 1979–81, New Yorker, 1979–81, St. Regis, Gran Fury

1. Remove the center bezel.
2. Remove the radio to panel mounting screws.
3. Pull the radio out through the front face of the panel. Detach the antenna lead, ground strap, power wire, and speaker leads.

Cordoba

1. Disconnect the battery ground cable.
2. Remove the instrument cluster lower bezel.

3. Disconnect the antenna, speaker, and electrical leads.

4. Remove the nut holding the radio to the support bracket. The nut is at the back of the radio and on the side of tape player/radios.

5. Remove the screws holding the radio to the cluster housing from the front.

6. Remove the radio.

Gran Fury 1975–77, Monaco 1975–76, 1977 Royal Monaco

1. Disconnect the battery ground cable. Remove the instrument cluster bezel by placing the automatic transmission lever in 1 position, removing the ashtray and lighter, removing the screws under the lower bezel edge, pulling the top out, and disengaging the locking tabs.

2. Remove the sub bezel by removing the nylon attaching pins with pliers.

3. Remove the lamp assembly from the front of the monoaural radio.

4. Remove the radio to panel screws.

5. Remove the instrument panel upper cover, first pulling the rear edge up.

6. Disconnect the antenna and speaker wires. Remove the radio bracket mounting nut.

7. Pull the radio out and disconnect the wire.

Coronet, Charger

1. Disconnect the batter ground cable.

2. Remove the ashtray.

3. Remove the right radio mounting screw from the right cluster leg. You can reach the screw through the lower left corner of the ashtray housing.

4. Loosen the support bracket nut on the right side of the radio.

5. Pull the knobs off. Remove the mounting nuts from the panel.

6. Detach the antenna, speaker, and power wires.

7. Remove the radio.

Coronet, Charger, Fury, Magnum, 1977–78 Monaco

1. Disconnect the battery ground cable.

2. Remove the instrument cluster lower

bezel by removing the right remote control mirror mounting nut, removing the mounting screws, and pull it off.

3. Disconnect the power, speaker, and antenna leads.

4. Remove the nut holding the radio to the support bracket at the rear. On tape player/radios, it is on the side.

5. Remove the radio mounting screws from the front of the panel.

6. Remove the radio from the front of the panel.

Omni and Horizon

1. Remove the seven bezel attaching screws and open the glove compartment.

2. Remove the bezel, guiding the right end around the glove compartment and away from the panel.

3. Disconnect the radio ground strap and remove the two radio mounting screws.

4. Pull the radio from the panel and disconnect the wiring and antenna lead.

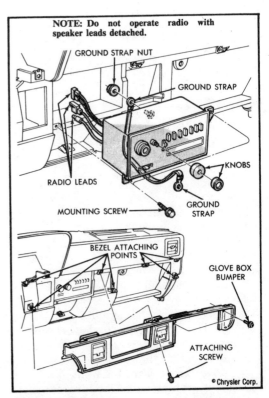

Omni and Horizon

Aries and Reliant, Dodge 400 and LeBaron

1. Remove the center bezel.

2. If equipped with a mono-speaker, remove the instrument panel top cover, speaker, and disconnect the wires from the radio.

3. Remove the two screws attaching the radio to the base panel.

4. Pull the radio thru the front of the base, then disconnect the wiring harness, antenna lead and ground strap.

FORD MOTOR CO.

Bobcat, Mustang II, Pinto

1. Disconnect the negative battery cable from the battery.

2. Remove the control knobs, discs, control shaft nuts and washers on Mustang II. Remove the panel trim brace cover on Pinto or Bobcat.

3. On the Mustang II, pull the ash try out to expose the lower mounting bolt. Remove the bolt.

4. Remove the radio rear support attaching nut or bolt.

5. On Pinto or Bobcat, remove the four screws attaching the bezel to the instrument panel opening.

6. Remove the radio from the instrument panel; out through the front on Pinto or Bobcat, or down from behind the instrument panel on Mustang II.

7. Disconnect the electrical lead, antenna lead, and speaker leads from the radio and remove the radio from the vehicle.

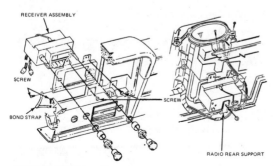

Bobcat, Mustang II

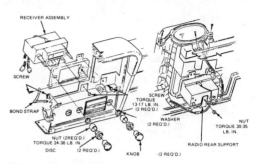

1975–77 Mustang II

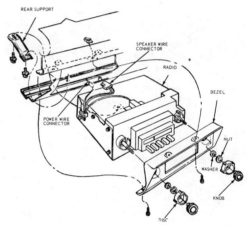

1975–77 Pinto

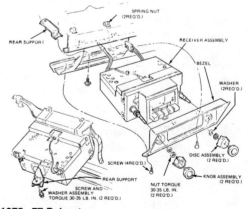

1975–77 Bobcat

Escort, EXP, Lynx, LN-7

1. Disconnect the negative battery cable. NOTE: *Remove the A/C floor duct if so equipped.*

2. Remove the ash tray and bracket.

3. Pull the knobs from the shafts.

4. Working under the instrument panel,

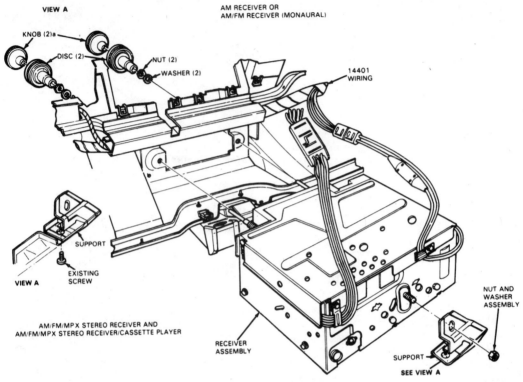

VIEW A

AM RECEIVER OR
AM/FM RECEIVER (MONAURAL)

KNOB (2)a
DISC (2)
NUT (2)
WASHER (2)
14401 WIRING

SUPPORT
EXISTING SCREW
VIEW A

AM/FM/MPX STEREO RECEIVER AND
AM/FM/MPX STEREO RECEIVER/CASSETTE PLAYER

RECEIVER ASSEMBLY

NUT AND WASHER ASSEMBLY

SUPPORT
SEE VIEW A

Escort, Lynx, EXP and LN-7

remove the support bracket nut from the radio chassis.

5. Remove the shaft nuts and washers.

6. Drop the radio down from behind the instrument panel. Disconnect the power lead, antenna, and speaker wires. Remove the radio.

Torino, Montego, Elite, LTD II, Cougar and Thunderbird Through 1979

1. Disconnect the battery.

2. Pull radio control knobs off shafts.

3. Remove radio support to instrument panel attaching screw.

4. Remove two bezel nuts from radio control shafts. Remove the rear support bracket, if so equipped.

5. Lower radio and disconnect antenna, speaker, and power leads. Remove radio.

6. To install, connect antenna, speaker and power leads to radio.

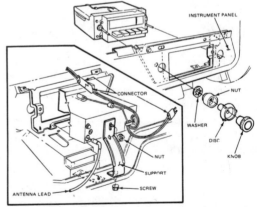

INSTRUMENT PANEL

CONNECTOR

NUT
WASHER
DISC
KNOB

NUT
SUPPORT
ANTENNA LEAD
SCREW

1975–77 Elite, Falcon, Fairlane, Torino, LTD II and 1977 Thunderbird

7. Position radio in instrument panel and install two bezel nuts.

8. Install radio support bracket to instrument panel attaching screw.

9. Connect battery.

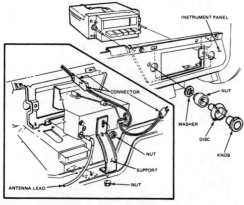

1975–77 Montego, 1975–77 Cougar

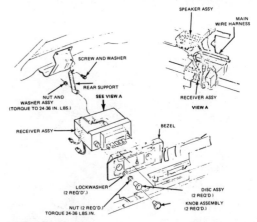

1975–76 Comet

Maverick and Comet

1. Disconnect the battery, and remove the seatbelt interlock module, if any, beneath the radio.

2. Remove radio rear support nut and lock washer.

3. Remove four radio to instrument panel retaining screws.

4. Pull radio from instrument panel and disconeect antenna, speaker, and power leads.

5. Remove radio.

6. Remove knob and disc assemblies from radio shafts.

7. Remove two bezel retaining nuts and remove bezel.

Ford and Mercury

1. Disconnect the battery ground cable.

2. On all-electronic radios, remove the radio-to-mounting plate screws and remove the mounting plate.

3. Remove the radio knobs, the screws that attach the bezel to the instrument panel, and remove the bezel.

4. Remove the radio mounting plate attaching screws (standard radios), and disengage the radio by pulling it from the lower rear support bracket.

5. Disconnect all the leads from the radio.

6. Remove the radio mounting plate and the rear upper support; remove the radio from the instrument panel.

7. Reverse the procedure to install.

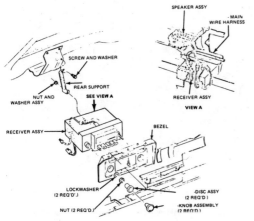

1975–77 Maverick

Thunderbird Through 1976

1. Disconnect the negative battery cable.

2. Remove the knobs from the radio shafts.

3. Remove the radio shaft nuts and the rear support attaching screw.

4. Disconnect the power lead, speaker wires and antenna lead, and remove the radio.

5. Remove the 2 screws attaching the Twilight Sentinel amplifier. Lower the amplifier.

6. Remove the air conditioning duct from beneath the radio.

7. Disconnect the radio rear support.

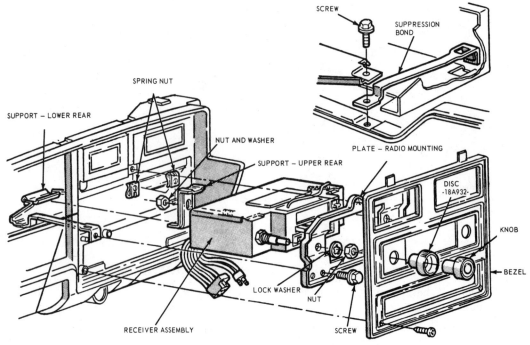

1975–77 Ford—other years similar

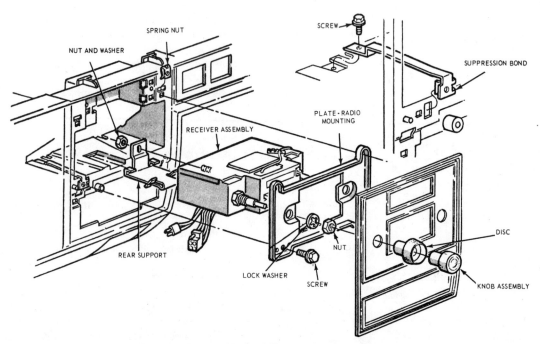

1975–77 Mercury

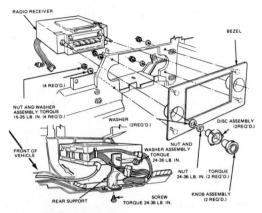

1975–76 Thunderbird

Granada, Monarch, Versailles Through 1980

1. Disconnect the negative battery cable.
2. Remove the headlight switch from the instrument panel. Remove the heater, air conditioner, windshield wiper/washer knobs, and radio knobs and discs.
3. Remove the six screws which attach the applique to the instrument panel and remove the applique. Disconnect the antenna lead-in cable from the radio.
4. Remove the four screws which attach the radio bezel to the instrument panel. Slide the radio and bezel out of the lower rear support bracket and instrument panel opening toward the interior far enough to disconnect the electrical connections, and remove the radio.

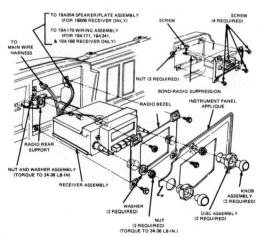

1975–77 Granada

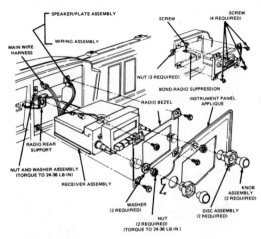

1975–77 Monarch

5. Remove the nut attaching the rear support bracket to the radio and remove the bracket. Remove the nuts and washer from the radio control shafts and remove the bezel.

Fairmont, Zephyr, Mustang, Capri, 1981–82 Granada and Cougar, Futura

1. Disconnect the negative battery cable. On models through 1978, remove the seat belt interlock module underneath the radio.
2. Disconnect the electrical, speaker, and antenna leads from the radio.
3. Remove the knobs, discs, and control shaft nuts and washers from the radio shafts.
4. On 1979 and later models, remove the ash tray receptacle and bracket.
5. Remove the rear support nut from the radio.
6. On 1979 and later models, remove the instrument panel lower reinforcement and the heater or air conditioning floor ducts.
7. Remove the radio from the rear support, and drop the radio down and out from behind the instrument panel.

1980 and Later Thunderbird and Cougar XR-7—1980 and Later, 1982 Lincoln Continental

1. Disconnect the negative battery cable.
2. Remove the radio knobs (pull off). Remove the center trim panel.

3. Remove the radio mounting plate screws. Pull the radio towards the front seat to disengage it from the lower bracket.

4. Disconnect the radio and antenna connections.

5. Remove the radio. Remove the nuts and washers (conventional radios) or mounting-plate screws (electronic radios) as necessary.

1975–77 Lincoln

1. Disconnect the battery ground cable.

2. Remove the radio knobs.

3. Remove and disconnect the map light. It is held by three screws.

4. Remove the steering column shroud, ashtray door pad, and instrument cluster panel pad. Open the glove box.

5. Remove the center register applique. It is held by three screws and two nuts.

6. Detach the lighter and glove box light connectors.

7. Remove the nut holding the radio bracket-to-instrument panel tab. Remove the three screws holding the bracket to the panel.

8. Pull the radio out and disconnect the power, speaker, and antenna leads.

9. Remove the nuts and washers from the control shafts to remove the mounting plate. The rear mounting bracket is held on with one nut.

10. Installation is the reverse.

1978–79 Lincoln

1. Disconnect the battery ground cable.

2. Remove the knobs. Remove the screws holding the radio bezel plate to the instru-

ment panel. Remove the screws holding the radio mounting plate.

3. Detach the radio from the lower rear support bracket.

4. Disconnect the power, antenna, and speaker leads.

5. Remove the mounting plate and rear upper support from the radio.

6. Reverse the procedure for installation.

Mark IV and V

1. Disconnect the negative battery cable.

2. Pull the radio control knobs off the radio shafts. Disconnect and lower the Twilight Sentinel amplifier, if equipped.

3. Remove the nuts from both radio con-

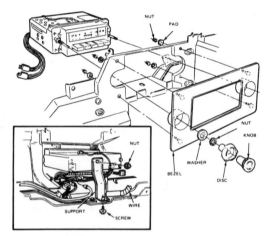

Continental Mark IV

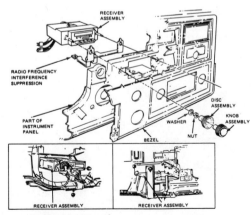

Continental Mark V

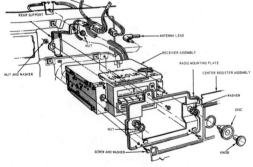

1975–77 Continental

trol shafts. Disconnect the air conditioning duct under the ardio.

4. Remove the radio rear support to panel attaching screw. On some 1976 and later models, this screw was replaced with a rivet. In order to remove the rivet you must drill it out with a ¼ in. drill bit. When you replace the radio, replace the rivet with a ¼ in. nut and bolt.

5. Disconnect the radio power wires. Disconnect the speaker wires at the connectors.

6. Disconnect the antenna lead and remove the radio.

Mark VI 1980 and Later

1. Disconnect the negative battery cable.
2. Remove the four radio plate-to-panel screws. Pull the radio with the front plate attached rearward until the rear bracket is clear.
3. Disconnect the wires from the chassis. If equipped with premium sound, remove the control assembly attaching nut and washer, remove the switch, and remove the illumination lamp socket from the front bracket.
4. Remove the radio with the front plate attached. Remove the four screws and remove the plate.

OLDSMOBILE

88, 98, Toronado—1975–76

1. Disconnect the negative battery cable.
2. On 1976 models, remove the lower trim pad.
3. Disconnect the wiring and the antenna lead.

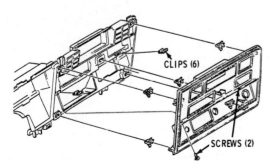

1977 88, 98 trim clips

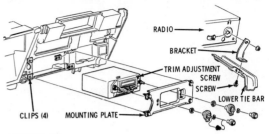

1977 88, 98

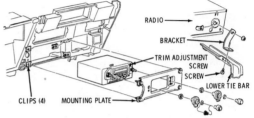

1978 and later 88, 98

4. On 1975 models, disconnect the throttle cable and remove the throttle lever and reinforcement.

5. Remove the support bracket-to-tie bar attaching screw.

6. Remove the knobs from the radio. Remove the two radio-to-instrument cluster attaching nuts.

7. Remove the radio from behind the instrument cluster.

88, 98, Toronado—1977–82

1. Disconnect the negative battery cable.
2. Remove the knobs from the radio and pull out the cigarette lighter.
3. Remove the two trim cover attaching screws and remove the cover.
4. Remove the radio bracket attaching screw from the lower tie bar.
5. Remove the four mounting plate screws and pull the radio out to obtain access to the electrical connections. Detach the wiring harness and the antenna lead.
6. Remove the mounting plate nuts and remove the radio. Installation is the reverse.

Cutlass—1975–77

1. Detach the cable from the negative battery terminal.

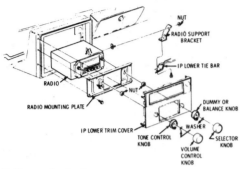

Cutlass—typical

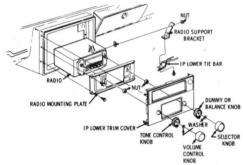

Toronado—typical

2. Remove the four screws which secure the steering column cover and separate it from the instrument panel.

3. Pull the knobs off the radio.

4. Unfasten the nuts from the front of the radio.

5. Remove its four retaining screws and then gently pull the right-hand control panel up and out.

6. Unfasten the radio support bracket screw.

7. Remove the four ashtray housing screws and take the housing off the tie-bar.

8. Disconnect the antenna and speaker wiring from the radio.

9. Remove the radio from behind the control panel.

Cutlass—1978-82

1. Disconnect the negative battery cable.

2. Remove the radio knobs. Pull the lower trim cover outward, off the retaining clips.

3. Remove the four mounting plate screws and the screw from the radio support bracket on the lower tie bar.

4. Pull the radio out and detach the wiring and the antenna lead.

Starfire—1975

1. Disconnect the battery.

2. Remove the clock set knob.

3. Remove the screws securing the instrument cluster bezel and remove the bezel.

4. Remove the glove compartment.

5. Remove the screws securing the instrument panel crash pad and remove the pad.

6. Pull the knobs off the radio shafts and unfasten the shaft retaining nuts.

7. Remove the two bottom screws from the radio bracket.

8. On models with A/C, remove the left lap cooler and duct.

9. Remove the two steering column bracket nuts and lower the column so that it rests on the driver's seat. Remove the screw which secures the cluster to the carrier, from the steering column bracket.

10. Unfasten the instrument cluster screws, wiring, speedometer cable, and pull the cluster out toward the driver's seat.

11. Remove the lower radio support-to-dash screw.

12. Working through the cluster opening, remove the radio leads and antenna cable.

13. Remove the radio.

Starfire—1976 and Later

1. Disconnect the battery ground cable.

2. Pull off the knobs and bezels.

3. Remove the shaft nuts and washers.

4. Remove the panel lower insulator assembly.

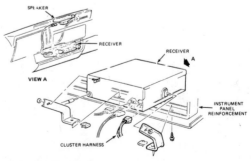

1976–77 Starfire

5. Detach the antenna lead from the back of the radio.

6. Remove the heater outlet duct on air conditioned cars.

7. Remove the two screws holding the radio to the panel brace.

8. Lower the radio, detach the speaker and power leads, and remove the mounts from the radio.

9. Installation is the reverse.

Omega Through 1979

1. Disconnect the battery.

2. Remove the knobs, washers, trim plate and nuts.

3. Disconnect the wiring.

4. Remove the screws or nuts from the rear mounting bracket. Lower the radio to remove.

5. Installation is the reverse.

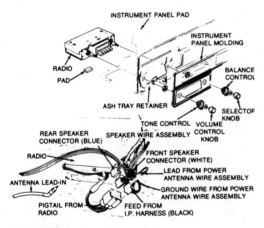

1980–82 Omega

Omega—1980 and Later

1. Remove the instrument panel molding.

2. Remove the ash tray receiver.

3. Remove the four screws attaching the ash tray assembly and remove the ash tray light bulb and socket assembly.

4. Pull the radio and ash tray retainer assembly out far enough to disconnect the radio wiring and remove the radio.

Firenza

1. Remove the instrument panel trim plate.

2. The radio mounting screws are located on the top and bottom of the radio. Remove the mounting screws.

3. Unplug the radio antenna and the electrical leads.

4. Remove the radio.

Ciera

See Chevrolet Celebrity.

PONTIAC

T-1000

Refer to the Chevrolet Chevette section.

Ventura and Phoenix Through 1979

1. Disconnect battery.

2. Remove radio knobs, bezels and hex nuts.

3. Remove support bracket bolt. Remove the Ventura and Phoenix radio sidebrace screw.

4. Disconnect electrical and antenna leads; remove radio from under dash.

LeMans, 1982 Bonneville

1. Disconnect the battery.

2. Remove the radio knobs and bezels.

3. Remove the upper and lower instrument panel trim plates.

4. Remove the two (1975–77) or four (1978–81) front radio retaining screws.

5. Remove the radio from the panel opening, disconnecting the electrical connections and the antenna lead on cars through 1977. For 1978 and later, open glove box door and lower by releasing spring clip. Pull the radio out after loosening rear, right side nut. Disconnect all wiring and remove the radio.

6. If the radio is to be replaced, remove the bushing from the rear of the radio and install it on the replacement radio.

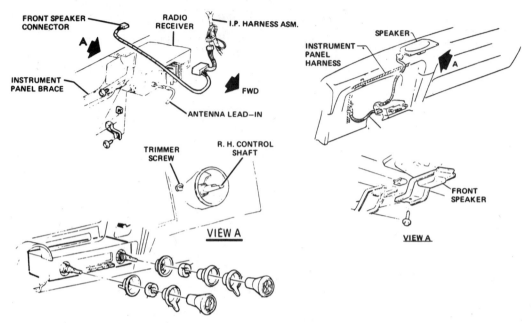

Ventura radio and front speaker

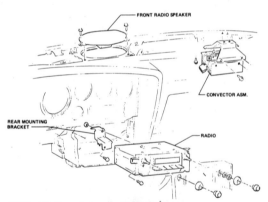

1975–77 Grand Am and LeMans

Grand Am and Grand LeMans

1. Disconnect the battery.

2. Remove the radio knobs and bezels and the retaining hex nut from the right-hand radio tuning shaft.

3. Remove the four retaining screws and the trim plate.

4. Remove the one front retaining screw and the mounting bracket screw.

5. Remove the radio and the mounting bracket from the dash, disconnecting the electrical connections and the antenna lead.

6. To install, reverse the removal procedure.

Astre and Sunbird

1. Remove battery ground cable.

2. Remove knobs, controls, washers and nuts from radio bushings.

3. Disconnect antenna lead, power connector, and speaker connectors from rear of receiver.

4. Remove two screws securing radio mounting bracket to instrument panel lower reinforcement and lift out radio receiver.

5. To install, reverse the removal procedure.

Phoenix—1980–82

1. Disconnect the negative battery cable.

2. Remove the center instrument panel trim plate.

3. Remove the radio attaching screws and pull the radio out to gain access to the wiring.

4. Disconnect the wiring. Remove the knobs and separate the face plate from the radio. Reverse to install.

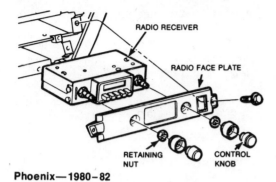

Phoenix—1980–82

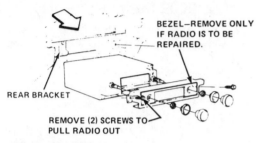

1978 and later Pontiac

Firebird

1. Disconnect the battery ground cable.
2. Remove the glove box and lower right A/C duct.
3. Remove the knobs and trim plate.
4. Disconnect all wiring.
5. Remove the radio and bracket through the passenger side of the panel.
6. To install reverse the procedure.

Firebird prior to 1982

Bonneville, Catalina, Grand Ville—through 1976

1. Disconnect the negative battery terminal, then remove the radio knobs and hex nuts.
2. Remove the upper and lower instrument panel trim plates and the lower front radio bracket.
3. Remove the glove box and disconnect the radio connections.
4. Loosen the side brace screw and slide the radio toward the front seat.

Bonneville, Catalina, Grand Ville—1977 and Later

1. Disconnect the negative battery terminal.
2. Remove the upper trimplate. Remove the radio trim plate by removing the two top screws, the ashtray assembly, disconnecting the lighter, and removing the ashtray bracket.
3. Remove the two radio screws.
4. Remove the radio through the instrument panel and detach all connectors.

Grand Prix

1. Disconnect the negative battery terminal.
2. Remove the knobs, bezels, and right-hand hex nut from the radio. On 1978 and later models, remove the upper and lower instrument panel trim plates.
3. Remove the four retaining screws and the radio trim plate.

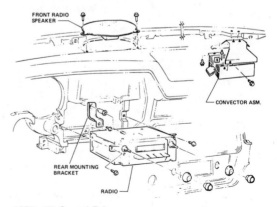

1975–77 Grand Prix

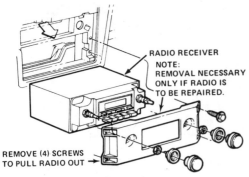

RADIO RECEIVER

NOTE:
REMOVAL NECESSARY
ONLY IF RADIO IS
TO BE REPAIRED.

REMOVE (4) SCREWS
TO PULL RADIO OUT →

1978 and later Grand Prix

4. Remove the one front retaining screw and the radio mounting bracket retaining screw (below radio). On 1978 and later models, open the glove box and loosen the rear nut at the right side of the radio.

5. Remove the radio and bracket as an assembly; disconnect the radio connections and antenna lead-in while the radio is pulled out.

J2000

See Cadillac Cimarron

6000

See Chevrolet Celebrity

IMPORT CARS

NOTE: *Many import car radios are dealer installed options. As such, installation procedures may vary slightly depending on the type of equipment installed.*
CAUTION: *See Notes and precautions on page 53.*

AUDI 4000/5000

1. Disconnect the negative battery cable.
2. On all 4000 models, remove the left and right covers under the instrument panel and then remove the bottom center console.
3. Remove the radio control knobs.
4. Remove the nuts from the radio control shafts.
5. Remove the screws for the center cover on the 4000 and the center console on the 5000.

6. Pull the cover/console away from the instrument panel slightly and disconnect the antenna lead, the power lead and the speaker leads.

7. Remove the radio support nuts and bolts and remove the radio.

BMW

1600-2, 2002 Series, 320i

1. Disconnect the negative battery cable.
2. Unscrew the shift lever and lift off the boot.
3. Remove the phillips head screws which retain the console to the dash and transmission tunnel.
4. Remove the phillips head screws which retain the left and right-hand side panels of the console to the radio mounting bracket. Remove the side panels, exposing the radio mounting bracket. (The radio mounting bracket houses the speaker.)
5. Disconnect the antenna cable from the radio. Disconnect the radio ground cable (if so equipped) from the left-hand heater mounting bolt. Disconnect the power lead for the radio from the existing plug located inline to the hazard warning switch.
6. Lift the radio mounting bracket forward. The radio may now be disconnected from the speaker by removing the speaker multiple plug from the back of the radio.
7. Pry off the radio control knobs exposing the mounting nuts. Unscrew the mounting nuts and remove the radio from its bracket.

2800, 3.0 Series, 530i, 528i, 630CSi, 633CSi, 733i

1. Remove the four screws from the outside of the underdash console while supporting the radio from underneath. Pull the unit out and lay it on the console.
2. Disconnect the aerial cable (large plug), the negative cable ("B−"), the speaker plugs (from the back of the unit) and the positive cable ("B+"—violet in color).

CAPRI

1. Remove the package tray, if any.
2. Remove the radio knobs and unscrew the retaining nuts.
3. Remove the wire connectors from the radio and remove the brackets from the rear of the radio.
4. Remove the radio.
5. Place the radio in position and install the brackets and the wiring connectors.
6. Install the package tray.

COLT AND CHALLENGER (DODGE)

1975–82 Rear Wheel Drive

1. Disconnect the battery ground cable. Remove glove box then loosen the knobs and attaching nuts on the front of the radio.
2. Remove speaker, antenna, and power wires from the back of the radio. Remove the radio attaching bracket and take out the radio.

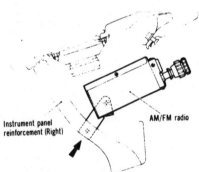

Instrument panel reinforcement (Right)

AM/FM radio

1975–77 Colt (rear wheel drive)

1979–82 Front Wheel Drive

1. Disconnect the battery ground cable. Remove the instrument cluster or instrument panel trim.
2. Remove the radio knobs from the radio panel
3. Disconnect the wiring harness. Remove the nuts from behind the knobs, the screw from the bracket and remove the radio (AM radio). Remove the bolts from under the

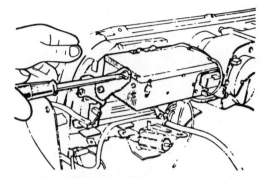

1979–82 Colt (front wheel drive)

brackets and remove the radio (AM/FM radio).

DATSUN

610, 710, 280ZX and F-10

1. Detach all electrical connections.
2. Remove the radio knobs and retaining nuts.
3. Remove the mounting screws, tip the radio down at the rear, and remove.

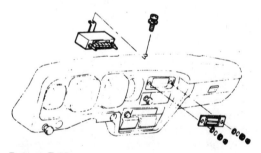

Datsun F-10

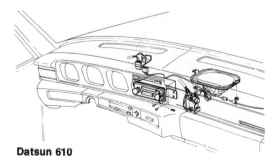

Datsun 610

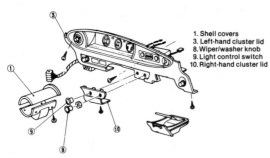

1. Shell covers
3. Left-hand cluster lid
8. Wiper/washer knob
9. Light control switch
10. Right-hand cluster lid

Datsun 710

B210, 1978–79 510, 1977–79 200SX, 810, 210

1. Remove the instrument cluster.
2. Detach all electrical connections.
3. Remove the radio knobs and retaining nuts.
4. Remove the rear support bracket.
5. Remove the radio.

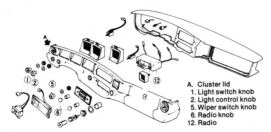

A. Cluster lid
1. Light switch knob
2. Light control knob
5. Wiper switch knob
6. Radio knob
12. Radio

Datsun B-210

200SX—1980 and Later

1. Disconnect the battery. Before removing the radio (audio assembly), you must remove the center instrument cluster which holds the heater controls, etc. Remove the two side screws in the cluster. Remove the heater control and the control panel. Remove the two bolts behind the heater control panel and the two bolts at the base of the cluster. Pull the cluster out of the way after disconnecting the lighter wiring and any other control cables.
2. Remove the radio knobs and fronting panel.
3. Remove the five screws holding the radio assembly in place.
4. Remove the radio after unplugging all connections.

310

1. Disconnect the battery ground cable.
2. Remove the center bezel.
3. Loosen and remove the screws retaining the radio in place.
4. Remove the radio and disconnect the antenna feeder cable, power lines and speaker connections.

280Z

The radio is mounted in the center console panel and the speaker in the left fender inner panel. The front face plate of the console must be removed to remove the radio.

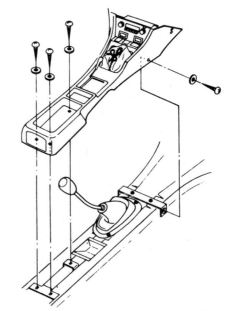

Datsun 280Z Console

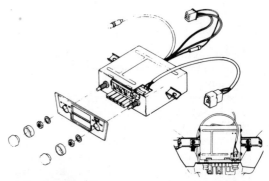

Datsun 280Z radio

FIAT

850

1. The dealer-installed radio is located either at the right side of the dashboard or in the center on some models.

2. Remove the radio knobs. If equipped with a trim panel, remove this also.

3. Remove the shaft nuts, spring washers, plastic panel, and flat washers. Flat washers are installed with the chamfered side toward the body.

4. Detach the speaker, antenna, and power leads.

5. Remove the support brace from the rear of the set.

6. If may be necessary to remove the speaker to provide clearance for set removal. If so, remove the speaker.

7. Remove the radio through the parcel shelf opening.

X1/9

The original dealer installed radio is housed in an L-shaped metal bracket above the center air outlet panel, covered by a plastic housing supplied with the installation kit.

1. Remove the radio knobs.

2. Remove the shaft nuts.

3. Remove the plastic cover panel held in place by the radio shaft nuts.

4. Remove the radio from the L-shaped bracket.

5. Disconnect the antenna, power and speaker leads and remove the radio.

6. If desired, the radio support bracket can also be removed.

124 and Spider 2000 (Except Special and Wagon)

1. Remove the radio knobs.

2. Remove the shaft nuts and washers.

3. Remove the support plate (if equipped).

4. Disconnect the speaker, antenna and power leads.

5. Disconnect the rear support brace, if any.

6. Remove the radio from the dash, down and to the right.

124 Special and Wagon

1. Remove the attaching screws from the center console.

2. On some models, the defogger switch and the defogger "ON" indicator light are located in the center console. Pull the console slightly forward and disconnect the defogger and the radio leads.

3. Remove the console from beneath the dash.

4. Remove the radio knobs, washers and shaft nuts.

5. Remove the trim plate, if equipped.

6. Disconnect the rear radio support(s) and remove the radio from the console.

128 and Strada

The dealer installed radio is housed in a panel to the right of the ash tray.

1. Remove the radio knobs.

2. Remove the shaft nuts.

3. Remove the radio trim plate from the dash.

4. Remove the radio after disconnecting the power, antenna and speaker leads.

131 and Brava

The dealer installed optional radio is dash mounted over the heater and A/C controls.

1. Remove the radio nuts.

2. Remove the plastic radio/heater control cover by gently prying it loose. It snaps into place.

3. Remove the 2 screws at the right-hand and left-hand side of the heater and A/C controls. This panel also supports the radio.

4. Remove the radio shaft and maneuver the panel aside.

5. Disconnect the speaker, antenna and power leads and remove the radio from the support panel, through the front of the dash.

FIESTA (FORD)

NOTE: *It is recommended that the battery ground cable be disconnected before the radio is removed.*

The radio is mounted to the bottom of the instrument panel. Remove the hot wire and antenna lead from the rear of the radio. Remove the attaching screws and brackets and remove the radio.

HONDA

Civic

1. Remove the screw which holds the rear radio bracket to the back tray underneath the instrument panel. Then remove the wing nut which holds the radio to the bracket and remove the bracket.

2. Remove the control knobs, hex nuts, and trim plate from the radio control shafts.

3. Disconnect the antenna and speaker leads, the bullet type radio fuse, and the white lead connected directly over the radio opening.

4. Drop the radio out, bottom first, through the package tray.

Accord and Prelude

1. Remove the center lower trim panel beneath the radio. Then remove the three radio lower bracket retaining screws.

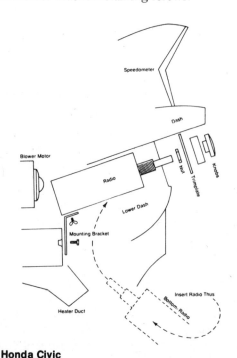

Honda Civic

Honda Accord

2. Pull off the radio knobs and remove the radio shaft nuts.

3. Remove the heater fan switch knob, the heater lever knobs, the heater control bezel, and the heater control center trim panel. Disconnect the cigarette lighter leads.

4. Pull out the radio from the front, and disconnect the power, speaker, and antenna leads.

MAZDA

RX-3

1. Unfasten the two upper and the two lower screws which secure the center panel to the dashboard.

2. Remove the ashtray.

3. Remove the knobs from both the radio and the heater controls.

4. Tip the center panel forward.

5. Disconnect the power, speaker, and antenna leads from the radio.

6. Slip the radio out from behind the panel.

RX-4

1. Remove mounting screws and remove right (passenger's) side console cover.

2. Disconnect power connector and unscrew aerial connector.

3. Remove rear mounting bolt.

4. Pull off radio knobs. Support radio assembly from the rear while removing mounting bezel nuts. Pull the unit back so shafts clear the front of the console, and slide the unit out the right side.

Cosmo

1. Pull off radio knobs. Remove radio bezel nuts.
2. Disconnect radio power connector and unscrew aerial connector.
3. Support radio while removing rear mounting bolt.
4. If necessary disconnect additional connectors that may be in the way, and then tilt the rear of the radio upward, pull it backward (or toward the front of the car) until the knob shafts clear the console, and remove out one side.

808

1. Pull off radio knobs. Remove radio bezel nuts.
2. Disconnect radio power connector and unscrew aerial connector.
3. Remove rear radio bracket mounting nut while supporting radio.
4. Pull the back end of the radio slightly downward and to the rear until knob shafts clear the dash panel, and then pull the unit down and out from behind the panel.

GLC

1. Remove the crash pad, meter hood, and wood grain center panel.
2. Disconnect the (−) cable from the battery. Then, remove attaching screws from either side of the dash panel, and pull the radio out. Disconnect aerial wiring, power connector, and speaker connector, and pull the radio out of the dash.

626

1. Disconnect the negative battery cable.
2. Remove the ashtray, Radio knobs, heater control lever knob, and the fan control switch knob.
3. Remove the center panel attaching screws and pull the center panel rearward.
4. Remove the radio attaching screws and disconnect the antenna.

RX-7

1. Disconnect the negative battery cable.
2. Remove the center panel.
3. Disconnect the radio wiring and the antenna cable.
4. Remove the attaching screws and remove the radio.

MERCEDES-BENZ

All Models

Mercedes-Benz radio removal is similar for all models, although there are several types of rear support brackets.
1. Disconnect the battery.
2. Remove the radio knobs and switch lever.
3. Remove the radio trim plate.
4. Remove the screw and radio support bracket. Some models may use a right and left-hand bracket.
5. Remove the radio part way and disconnect the speaker, antenna and power leads. Disconnect the fader.
6. Some Mercedes-Benz radios use remote power packs, which can be removed if desired. The power pack is usually located on the right side of the firewall next to the heat exchanger or behind the glove compartment on the existing air flap screws.

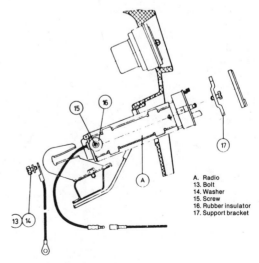

A. Radio
13. Bolt
14. Washer
15. Screw
16. Rubber insulator
17. Support bracket

Mercedes 450SL, 450SLC

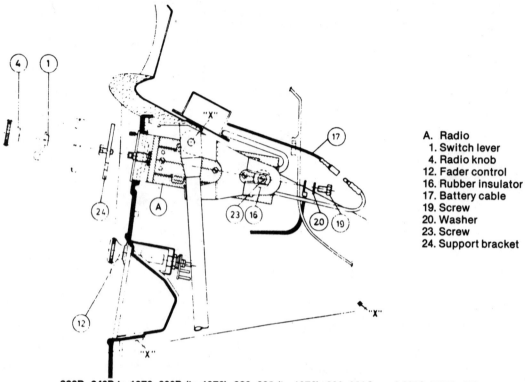

A. Radio
 1. Switch lever
 4. Radio knob
12. Fader control
16. Rubber insulator
17. Battery cable
19. Screw
20. Washer
23. Screw
24. Support bracket

220D, 240D to 1976, 300D (to 1976), 220, 230 (to 1976), 280, 280C, and 280S (1970–72)

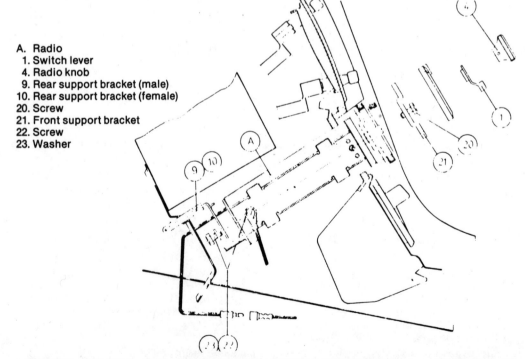

A. Radio
 1. Switch lever
 4. Radio knob
 9. Rear support bracket (male)
10. Rear support bracket (female)
20. Screw
21. Front support bracket
22. Screw
23. Washer

230 (1977), 240D (1977), 300D (1977), 280S (1975–77), 280SE (1977), 280E, 280C, and 280S (1970–72)

7. Remove the radio from the dash through the front.

MG

All Models

NOTE: *MG radios are dealer installed options. The following procedure is typical.*

1. Remove the control knobs.
2. Remove the nut covers and shaft nuts.
3. Remove the trim plate and chrome ring.
4. Disconnect the antenna, speakers and fused power lead.
5. Remove the optional rear support bracket.
6. Slide the radio out of the console opening. Remove the back-up plate from behind the dash. There are also 2 spacers, one on each shaft, secured with nuts.

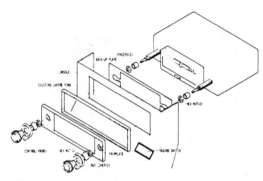

MG—All models

ISUZU (OPEL)

Disconnect negative battery cable.

1. Remove ash tray and tray support. Remove radio knobs by pulling off.
2. Remove retainer screws from under dash.
4. Disconnect electrical connectors and lead-in cable and take the radio out through the back of the dash.

OPEL

1900, Opel, Manta and Rallye

On the Opel and Rallye, the glove box and right defroster duct must be removed and the radio installed or removed through the glove box opening.

1. Disconnect the battery ground cable and the antenna and speaker connectors from the radio.
2. Remove the knobs from the radio and unbolt the mounting nuts.
3. Remove the receiver bracket lower screw from the receiver, loosen the upper bolt approximately 3 turns and slide out the radio.
4. Installation is the reverse of removal.

GT

1. Disconnect the battery.
2. Remove the access trim plug from the right side of the console.
3. Remove the hex head screw with an 8 mm socket through the access hole.
4. Remove the access trim cover on the left side of the console.
5. Remove the tear-lock bolts by first drilling a $3/16$ in. hole in the bolt and then using a ¼ in. bolt extractor.
6. Disconnect the white ignition and black turn signal wire set plugs.
7. Support the steering column, assembly and remove the two attaching bolts.
8. Disconnect the speedometer cable.
9. Remove the 6 instrument cluster retaining screws and pull the panel straight out.
10. Disconnect the radio harness plug and antenna lead from the back of the radio.
11. Remove the knobs from the radio.
12. Remove the radio control shaft retaining nuts while supporting the radio and then remove the radio.

PORSCHE

911

1. Disconnect the battery.
2. Disconnect the antenna, power and speaker leads from the radio and/or power pack.
3. Remove the radio knobs.
4. Remove the trim plate.
5. Remove the support bracket, secured by screws.
6. Remove the shaft nuts.

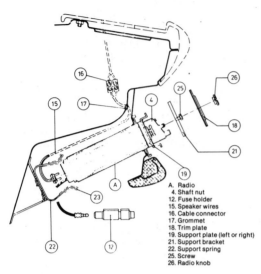

A. Radio
  4. Shaft nut
12. Fuse holder
15. Speaker wires
16. Cable connector
17. Grommet
18. Trim plate
19. Support plate (left or right)
21. Support bracket
22. Support spring
25. Screw
26. Radio knob

Porsche 911, 912

7. Unsnap the right and left-hand supports.

8. Disconnect the support spring (rear of radio) from its mounts on the firewall. The spring is removed with the radio.

9. Remove the radio down and out from beneath the dash.

914, 914/6

1. Disconnect the battery.

2. Unplug the power lead from the fuse box.

3. Unplug the antenna and speaker plugs from the power pack.

4. Remove the radio knobs and cover plate.

5. Remove the support bracket.

6. Disconnect the support spring at the rear of the radio from its mount on the firewall. The spring is removed with the radio.

7. Remove the radio from the dash.

924, 928

1. Disconnect the battery ground cable.

2. Remove the radio knobs.

3. Release the radio bezel by pressing the springs in the shaft openings outward to their stops.

4. Remove the bezel.

5. Remove the nuts on the shafts.

6. Loosen the brackets and pull the radio out.

7. Disconnect the fuse, ground, speaker, and antenna wires. Remove the radio.

A. Radio
B. Power pack
 1. Switch lever
 3. Fuse box
 4. Radio knob
 6. Trim plate
 7. Support bracket
 8. Support spring
 9. Mounting strap
11. Battery cable
12. Ground cable
13. Left speaker cable
14. Right speaker cable
15. Connection cable
20. Screw
21. Washer

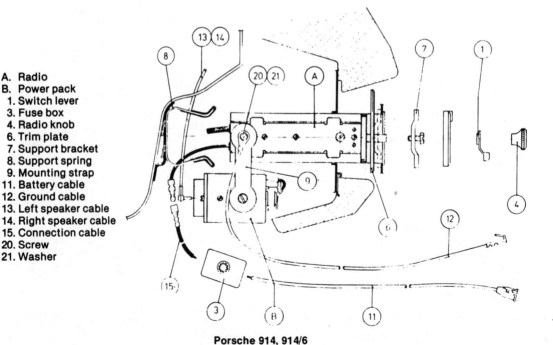

Porsche 914, 914/6

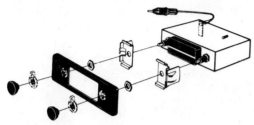

Porsche 924

PEUGEOT

1. Remove the console cover.
2. Remove the radio knobs and retaining nuts from the front of the radio.
3. Remove any brackets from the back of the radio and detach the power lead, antenna lead and speaker wires.

PLYMOUTH

Arrow, Champ and Sapporo

See Dodge Colt and Challenger

SUBARU

1975–76

1. Disconnect the negative (−) battery cable.
    NOTE: *Steps 2 and 3 do not apply to 1976 models.*
2. Use a phillips screwdriver with a short shank to remove the screws holding the speaker grille down. Remove the grille.
3. Disconnect the speaker lead from the radio connector.
4. Remove the instrument cluster bezel screws at the radio end.
5. Remove its screws and lift out the console, if so equipped.
6. Pull the knob off the fresh air lever, unfasten the two securing screws at either end, and remove the center outlet grille.
7. Pull both knobs off the radio shafts.
8. Remove the ash tray. Pull the knobs off the heater controls.
9. Remove the nuts from the radio control shafts.

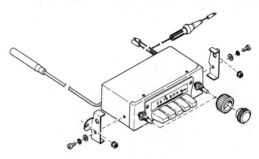

Subaru—typical

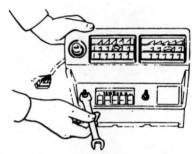

Removing Subaru radio mounting nuts

10. Remove the screws which secure the radio surround panel. Remove the panel.
11. Remove the radio bracket screws.
12. Disconnect the radio leads and pull the radio out of the dash.

1977–82

1. Disconnect the cable from the negative terminal of the battery.
2. Remove the center console assembly by removing the mounting screws and disconnecting the wire harness and antenna cable.
3. Pull off the radio control knobs.
4. Remove the radio mounting nuts from the control stems.
5. Remove the radio mounting screws from the back of the radio.
6. Lift out the radio.

TOYOTA

Celica and Cressida

1. Remove the knobs from the radio.
2. Remove the nuts from the radio control shafts.

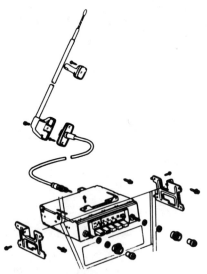

Toyota Celica—prior to '82

3. Detach the antenna lead from the jack on the radio case.

4. Remove the cowl air intake duct.

5. Detach the power and speaker leads.

6. Remove the radio support nuts and bolts.

7. Remove the radio from beneath the dashboard.

8. Remove the nuts which secure the speaker through the service hole in the top of the glove box.

9. Remove remainder of the speaker securing nuts from above the radio mounting location.

10. Remove the speaker.

Corolla—1975–82

1. Remove the two screws from the top of the dashboard center trim panel.

2. Lift the center panel out far enough to gain access to the cigarette lighter wiring and disconnect the wiring. Remove the trim panel.

3. Unfasten the screws which secure the radio to the instrument panel braces.

4. Lift out the radio and disconnect the leads from it. Remove the radio.

Carina

1. Remove the center air outlet from under the dash.

2. Unfasten the radio control mounting bracket.

3. Remove the radio control knobs and then the securing nuts from the control shafts.

4. Detach the speaker, and the power and antenna leads from the radio.

5. Withdraw the radio from underneath the dashboard.

6. Unfasten the speaker securing nuts and remove the speaker.

Tercel

1. Disconnect the negative battery terminal.

2. Disconnect the antenna.

3. Disconnect the electrical connector.

4. Remove the radio knobs and remove the face plate.

5. Remove the radio.

Corona—1975–82
INSTRUMENT PANEL—MOUNTED

1. Remove the two screws securing the instrument cluster surround and remove the surround.

2. Remove the knobs from the heater controls and remove the heater control face.

3. Remove the four screws which secure the center trim panel (two are behind the heater control opening).

4. Remove the radio knobs and remove the center trim panel.

5. Remove the four screws which secure the radio bracket.

6. Pull the radio far enough out to remove the antenna, power, and speaker leads.

7. Remove the radio.

CONSOLE—MOUNTED

1. Remove the screws which secure the console and remove the console, by lowering the armrest rearward and lifting up on the center of the console.

2. Unplug the radio and disconnect the antenna lead.

3. Remove the radio knobs.

4. Remove the radio bracket and then remove the radio.

Mark II/6

Mark II—1975–79

1. Remove the instrument cluster housing as detailed in the appropriate section below.
2. Remove the heater control panel assembly.
3. Unfasten the two radio securing bolts.
4. Detach all of the radio leads.
5. Withdraw the radio.

TRIUMPH

All Models Except TR-7

NOTE: *Triumph radios are dealer installed options. The following procedure is typical.*

1. Remove the radio knobs.
2. Remove the nut covers and shaft nuts.
3. Remove the trim plate.
4. Disconnect speaker antenna and power leads. Remove the optional rear support bracket.
5. Disconnect the light bar lead.
6. Remove the radio from the dash. One tublar spacer is secured to each shaft with a nut.

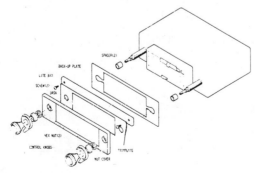

Triumph TR-6

7. Remove the back-up plate from behind the dash.
8. Installation is the reverse of removal.

TR-7

1. Remove the radio control knobs.
2. Remove the dummy parcel tray (if equipped).
3. Remove the vent, heat, air and screen knobs from the console panel.
4. Remove the 2 screws above the heater and air controls.
5. Remove the screw from each side of the console (if equipped).
6. Remove the screw holding the light bar to the console.
7. Pull the console up and rearward to remove it.
8. Remove the nut covers and nuts from the radio shafts.
9. Disconnect the antenna, speaker and power leads.
10. Remove the optional rear support bracket.
11. Remove the radio trim plate.
12. Remove the radio.
13. Remove the back-up plate.

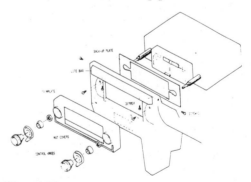

Triumph TR-7

VOLKSWAGEN

All Models Except Rabbit, Dasher, Scirocco, Jetta

NOTE: *On Type 3 and 4 models, it is necessary to loosen the evaporator (without discharging the system).*

1. Remove the knobs from the radio.
2. If applicable, remove the fresh air con-

trol knobs and remove the fresh air control trim plate.

3. Remove the nuts from the radio control shafts.

4. Detach the antenna, speaker and power leads.

5. Remove the radio support nuts/bolts, and if equipped the support strap.

6. Remove the radio from the dashboard.

Rabbit, Scirocco, Dasher, Jetta

1. Remove the knobs from the radio.

2. Remove the nuts from the radio control shafts.

3. Detach the antenna lead from the jack on the radio case.

CAUTION: *Never operate the radio without a speaker; severe damage to the output transistor will result. If the speaker must be replaced, use a speaker of the correct impedance (ohms) or else the output transistors will be damaged and require replacement.*

4. Detach the power and speaker leads.

5. Remove the radio support nuts and bolts.

6. Withdraw the radio from beneath the dashboard.

VOLVO

All Models

1. Disconnect the negative battery cable.

2. Remove the radio control knobs. Remove the control shaft retaining nuts.

3. Disconnect the speaker wires, the power

lead (either at the fuse box or the in-line fuse connection), and the antenna cable from its jack on the radio.

4. Remove the hardware which attaches the radio to its mounting (support) bracket(s), and slide it back and down from the dash.

TRUCKS AND VANS

CAUTION: *See Notes and precautions on page 53.*

CHEVROLET AND GMC

Blazer, Jimmy and Pick-Ups

1. Remove the negative battery cable and the control knobs, bezels, and nuts from the radio control shafts.

2. On AM radios, remove the support bracket stud nut and its lockwasher.

3. On AM/FM radios, remove the support bracket-to-instrument panel screws.

4. Lifting the rear edge of the radio, push the radio forward until the control shafts clear the instrument panel. Then lower the radio far enough so that the electrical connections can be disconnected.

5. Remove the power lead, speaker, and antenna wires and then pull out the unit.

Vans

1. Disconnect the ground cable from the battery.

2. Remove the engine cover.

3. Remove the air cleaner from the carburetor.

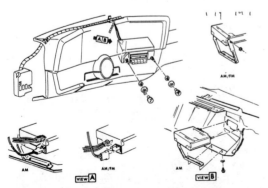

Blazer, Jimmy, Pick-Ups—1975 and later

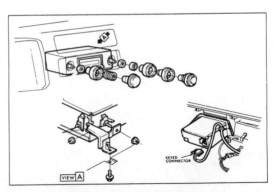

Chevy and GMC Vans 1978 and later

4. On models through 1977, remove the stud in the carburetor which holds the air cleaner.

5. Cover the carburetor with a clean rag.

6. Remove the knobs, washers and nuts from the front of the radio.

7. Remove the rear bracket screw and bracket from the radio.

8. Remove the radio through the engine access area. Lower the radio far enough to detach the wiring.

9. Remove the radio.

LUV

1. Disconnect the battery ground cable.

2. Remove the ash tray and ash tray plate.

3. Remove the tuner and volume control knobs, jam nuts, washers and face panel.

4. Remove the screws from the front and rear mounting brackets.

5. Disconnect the electrical connections, antenna lead and remove the radio. Remove the front mounting brackets from the radio.

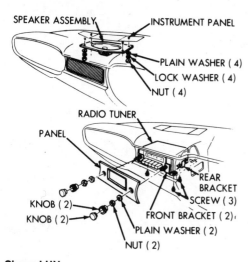

Chevy LUV

DATSUN

1975–79

1. Pull the knobs off the radio control shafts.

2. Remove the radio retaining nuts and washer from the radio control shafts.

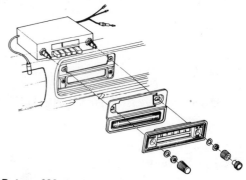

Datsun 620

3. Remove the bezel plate from the front of the radio.

4. Disconnect the antenna cable and the power and speaker wires from under the instrument panel.

5. Remove the radio from the instrument panel.

6. Install the radio in the reverse order of removal.

1980–82

1. Disconnect the battery ground.

2. Remove the ash tray and heater/air conditioner control panel.

3. Disconnect the wiring plug at the back of the radio.

4. Remove the plug covering the mounting screws, remove the screws and pull the radio from the dash.

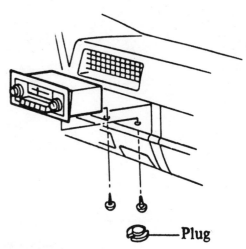

Datsun 720 1980–82

5. Disconnect the wiring harness and the antenna.

DODGE AND PLYMOUTH

All Models Except Rampage, Arrow and D-50

1975–77

1. Disconnect the negative battery cable.
2. Remove the mounting strap and remove the glove box door.
4. Remove the glove box mounting screws and pull the box out of the instrument panel.
5. Remove the radio bezel mounting nuts and remove the bezel.
6. Remove the radio-to-instrument panel attaching bolts and push the radio in to release the mounting tabs.
7. Working through the glove box opening, disconnect the antenna wire from the radio. Remove the right defroster distribution duct on vans equipped with A/C. Remove the radio rear support bracket nut, tilt the unit up and pull it out to release it from the support bracket. Disconnect the electrical and speaker wires.
8. Remove the radio through the glove box door. If the van is equipped with A/C, remove the radio through the duct opening.

1978 AND LATER

1. Disconnect the negative battery cable.
2. Remove the seven instrument panel and bezel attaching screws. Pull the bezel off the retaining clips.
3. Remove the five instrument cluster screws.
4. Pull the cluster out far enough to gain access to the speedometer cable. Push the cable spring clip toward the cluster and disconnect the cable.
5. Remove the right and left printed circuit board multiple connectors.
6. Remove the instrument cluster.

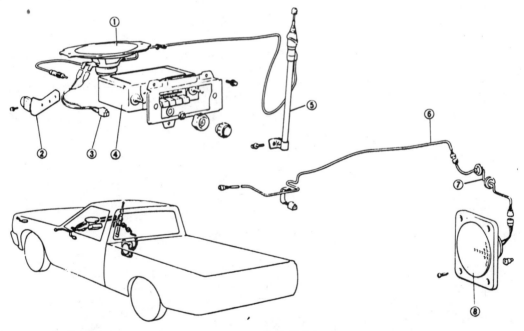

1. Speaker
2. Radio stay
3. Speaker wiring harness
4. AM radio
4. AM/FM MPX radio (for sports model)

5. Antenna
6. Speaker wiring harness (for sports model)
7. Door wiring harness (for sports model)
8. Speaker (for sports model)

Dodge D-50 and Arrow Pick-Up

7. Remove the radio mounting screws.

8. Remove the ground strap screw.

9. Pull the radio out of the instrument panel and disconnect the wiring.

D-50 (Dodge), Arrow (Plymouth) and Mitsubishi

1. Remove the instrument cluster bezel.

2. Remove the radio bracket attaching screws from the instrument panel, and remove the radio bracket.

3. Pull the radio out slightly, disconnect the antenna lead-in, speaker connector and the power supply connector.

4. Take out the radio.

Rampage

See Dodge Omni under domestic cars.

FORD

Vans

1975–82

1. Detach the battery ground cable.

2. Remove the heater and A/C control knobs. Remove the lighter.

3. Remove the radio knobs and discs.

4. If the truck has a lighter, snap out the name plate at the right side to remove the panel attaching screw.

5. Remove the five finish panel screws.

6. Very carefully pry out the cluster panel in two places.

7. Detach the antenna lead and speaker wires.

8. Remove the two nuts and washers and the mounting plate.

9. Remove the four front radio attaching

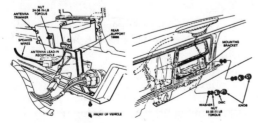

Ford Vans—typical

screws. Remove the rear support nut and washer and remove the radio.

Pick-Ups 1975–82

1. Disconnect the battery ground cable.

2. On 1975–79 models, remove the ash tray and bracket.

3. Disconnect the antenna, speakers and radio lead.

4. Remove the bolt attaching the radio rear support to the lower edge of the instrument panel.

5. On 1975–78 models equipped with air conditioning, disconnect the left A/C duct hose from the A/C plenum.

6. Remove the knobs and discs from the radio control shafts.

7. Remove the retaining nuts from the control shafts and remove the bezel.

8. Remove the nuts and washers from the control shafts and remove the radio from the panel.

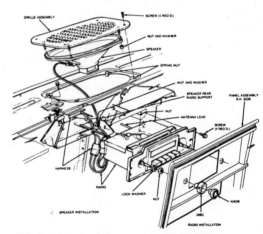

Ford Pick-Up (typical) and '78–'82 Bronco

Bronco

1975–77

1. Disconnect the radio lead wire at the receptacle on the fuse panel.

2. Disconnect the speaker leads at the receptacle on the underside of the radio chassis.

3. Disconnect the antenna lead at the receptacle on the right side of the radio chassis.

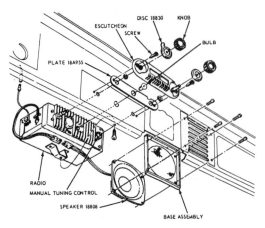

1975–77 Bronco

4. Remove (pull) the volume control and the manual tuning control knobs from the shafts.

5. Remove the screws that retain the dial assembly to the instrument panel and remove the dial assembly.

6. Remove the retaining nuts and the retaining plate that secure the radio to the instrument panel.

7. Remove the radio bottom support bracket retaining screw and remove the radio assembly from the instrument panel.

1978–82

1. Disconnect the battery ground cable.

2. On 1978–79 models, remove the ash tray and bracket.

3. Disconnect the antenna, speakers and radio lead.

4. Remove the bolt attaching the radio rear support to the lower edge of the instrument panel.

5. On 1978 models equipped with air conditioning, disconnect the left A/C duct hose from the A/C plenum.

6. Remove the knobs and discs from the radio control shafts.

7. Remove the retaining nuts from the control shafts and remove the bezel.

8. Remove the nuts and washers from the control shafts and remove the radio from the panel.

Courier

1975–78

1. Remove the ash tray, ash tray retainer and rear retainer support. Remove the heater control knobs, heater control bezel and right-hand defroster hose.

2. Remove the heater control and position it to the left.

3. Remove the radio chassis rear support bracket.

4. Bend the bracket down 90°.

5. Remove the radio knobs, attaching nuts and bezel.

6. Pull the chassis forward until the control shafts clear the holes in the instrument panel. Disconnect the speaker wires, power lead and antenna lead. Rotate the chassis so that the control shafts point upward and lower the radio.

1979–82

1. Disconnect the negative battery cable.

2. Pull off the heater control knobs, the instrument light brightness control knob, and the radio knobs.

3. Remove the ring nut and fiber washer for the brightness control. Remove the radio attaching nuts (shaft nuts). Remove the four screws for the meter hood (instrument trim panel) and remove the hood.

4. Slide the radio to the left until the rear support pin clears the support bracket. Pull the radio out from the instrument panel far enough to gain access to the wires at the rear of the radio chassis.

5. Disconnect the power lead, speaker leads and the antenna cable. Remove the radio.

INTERNATIONAL HARVESTER

1. Disconnect the negative battery cable.

2. Remove the bolts which hold the radio to the radio support.

3. Remove the attaching screws which hold the radio cover bezel to the instrument panel.

4. Pull the radio from the instrument panel and disconnect the radio lead wires.

5. Remove the radio from the car.

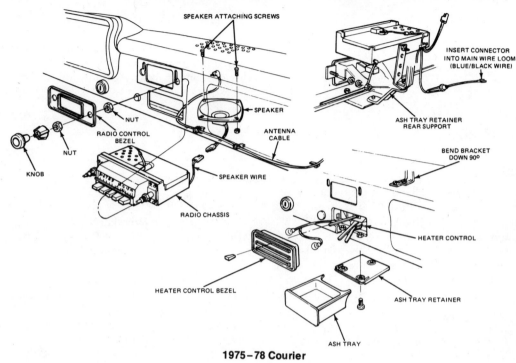

1975–78 Courier

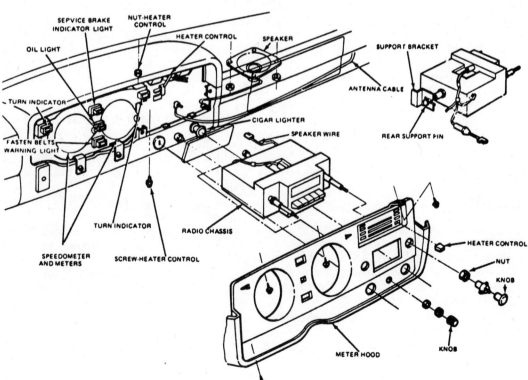

1979 and later Courier

ISUZU P'UP

See Chevrolet LUV in this section

JEEP

CJ Models, Cherokeee and Wagoneer

1975

The only radio available on CJ models was a simple, under-dash unit similar to previous dealer installed options. Removal and Installation are obvious.

On Wagoneer and Cherokee models, the radio is accessible after removing the glove box door, liner and lock striker. The radio is unbolted and removed through the glove box.

1976 AND LATER

1. Disconnect the battery ground cable.
2. Remove the control knobs, nuts, and bezel.
3. On 1976 and early 1977 models, you may have to detach the defroster hose. With air conditioning, remove the screws and lower the assembly.
4. Disconnect the radio bracket from the instrument panel.
5. Tilt the radio down and remove it toward the steering wheel.
6. Detach the antenna, speaker, and power wires.

MAZDA

B-1600

1. Remove the ash tray, ash tray retainer and rear retainer support. Remove the heater control knobs, heater control bezel and right-hand defroster hose.
2. Remove the heater control and position it to the left.
3. Remove the radio chassis rear support bracket.
4. Bend the bracket down 90°.
5. Remove the radio knobs, attaching nuts and bezel.

6. Pull the chassis forward until the control shafts clear the holes in the instrument panel. Disconnect the speaker wires, power lead and antenna lead. Rotate the chassis so that the control shafts point upward and lower the radio.

B-2000

See Ford Courier

Rotary Pick-Up

1. Remove the radio knobs.
2. Remove the radio shaft nuts.
3. Remove the radio trim panel.
4. If necessary, remove the center panel by removing the heater control knobs, cigarette lighter, the nut attaching the panel resistor to the center panel, the resistor wiring and the 2 screws attaching the center panel to the instrument panel.
5. Remove the radio attaching nuts.
6. Disconnect the power, speaker and antenna leads.
7. Remove the radio through the dash.

TOYOTA

1978 and Earlier Except Land Cruiser

1. Remove the knobs from the radio.
2. Remove the nuts from the radio control shafts.
3. Detach the antenna lead from the jack on the radio case.
4. Detach the power and speaker leads.
5. Remove the radio support nuts and bolts.
6. Remove the radio from beneath the dashboard.

Installation is the reverse of removal.

1979 And Later Except Land Cruiser

1. Disconnect the negative battery cable from the battery.

2. Remove steering column upper and lower covers.

3. Remove the five screws holding the instrument cluster trim panel and remove trim panel.

4. Remove the knobs from the radio and remove the securing nuts from the control shafts.

5. Remove the heater/air conditioner knobs from their control arms. Do not remove the blower fan control knob.

6. Remove the two screws holding the heater control dash light. Remove the ashtray and remove all of the screw holding the center facade onto the dash.

7. Pull the facade out, and carefully disconnect the cigarette lighter and the blower fan control at their plugs.

8. Unscrew any remaining screws holding the radio and pull it out part way. Disconnect the power source, speaker coupling, and antenna from the radio and remove through the dash.

Land Cruiser

1. Remove the knobs from the radio.

2. Remove the nuts from the radio control shafts.

3. Detach the antenna lead from the jack on the radio case.

4. Detach the power and speaker leads.

5. Remove the radio support nuts and bolts.

6. Withdraw the radio from beneath the dashboard.

VOLKSWAGEN RABBIT PICK-UP

See Volkswagen under import cars

GLOSSARY OF AUDIO TERMS

ACOUSTIC SUSPENSION A sealed-enclosure speaker design that uses the air inside the cabinet as a means of regulating the motion of the speaker disphragm(s).

AMPLIFIER In a hi-fi system, the electronic device that supplies power to a loudspeaker system(s). A *preamplifier* provides appropriate equalization and control facilities for various program sources (e.g. phone, FM, tape), and is included as part of an *integrated amplifier*.

ANTENNA The device used to intercept radio waves and convert them into electrical signals usable by a receiver or tuner.

BANDWIDTH The range over which the frequency or power response of a hi-fi component is substantially constant.

BASS The lowest portion of the perceived audio spectrum.

BASS REFLEX A loudspeaker system design in which a duct or port is used to increase speaker efficiency by utilizing the energy generated within the enclosure by the motion of the diaphragm or cone of the speaker(s).

BIAS In tape recording, the ultrasonic signal simultaneously applied to the tape during recording that is used to increase the strength and lower the distortion of the audio signal.

CASSEIVER A receiver in which a cassette deck is included as a single unit.

CASSETTE A compact enclosed reel-to-reel tape system introduced by Philips in 1964 as the "Compact Cassette" whose standardized formats have helped make it the dominant consumer tape medium.

CROSSOVER A frequency or electronic circuit at which frequency response is split into two or more paths. In a two-way speaker system the crossover frequency is the point at which woofer and tweeter signals are divided.

DECIBEL (db) A numerical (logarithmic) expression of acoustic or electrical ratios, such as the relative intensity of a sound or the relative strength of a signal. One db is usually considered the smallest change in sound level perceptible to the human ear.

DISTORTION Any alteration other than amplitude between the input and output of an electronic or acoustical device. *Harmonic distortion* changes the relationship between a tone and its overtones; *intermodulation distortion* creates sum and/or difference frequencies not present in the original tone. *Phase distortion* changes the timing between parts of a complex audio signal, and *transient distortion* affects the brief, staccato character associated primarily with percussive instruments.

DROPOUT The momentary loss or sharp reduction in level of recorded signal, usually caused by an imperfection in the magnetic coating on the tape.

EQUALIZATION The deliberate manipulation of frequency response to produce a desired effect. Equalization is used in the cutting and playback of records, in recording tapes, and in transmitting FM broadcasts. During playback, these various equalizations must be "compensated" by reciprocal equalization in the playback system. Equalization also refers to the modification of a music system's overall response to better suit its specific listening environment, whether by treble and bass tone controls or by a more specialized device.

FLUTTER Variations in the speed of a turntable or tape transport which, when pronounced, cause a wavering of musical pitch or a "muddy" sound quality.

FREQUENCY RESPONSE The variation, in decibels, between the relative amplitudes of differing frequencies (normally 20–20,000Hz) measured between the input and the output of a hi-fi component.

HERTZ The frequency of a signal, formerly known as cycles-per-second. A 1 kHz signal = 1,000 cps.

HUM A low-frequency noise, generally related to the power line or its harmonics, that intrudes into reproduced sound and mars listening quality.

IC (Integrated Circuit) A tiny chip of silicon which now does the work of numerous transistors, diodes, capacitors.

IF (Intermediate Frequency) The frequency to which a received radio signal is converted in a superheterodyne receiver.

IMPEDANCE Resistance to the flow of alternating currents such as the signals handled by high fidelity equipment. In general, the "output impedance" of home equipment is low (1/10 or less) compared to the "input impedance" of the component to which it is connected. The proper frequency response of phono cartridges and microphones may depend upon their being connected to a specified impedance, however.

LED (Light-Emitting Diode) An indicator that gives off light when an electric current passes through it, often used for volume level indicators on tape recorders, et al.

LOUDNESS CONTROL A volume control with special circuitry to compensate for the ear's differing sensitivity to tones at the extreme ends of the audio range listening at low volume levels. A typical loudness control boosts the bass (and sometimes treble), but leaves the midrange unaltered.

MIDRANGE The frequency range between bass and treble, typically 300–3000Hz.

NOISE Any extraneous sound or signal added in the recording, reproduction, or transmission of the original.

PCM (Pulse Code Modulation) A technique for recording or reproducing sound digitally.

RESONANCE In electronic or acoustic devices and systems, the tendency for excessive response to a particular frequency. Unwanted resonances in loudspeakers, for instance, cause audible colorations in sound quality.

REVERBERATION The perceived continuation of sound resulting from its reflection off exposed surfaces in a room.

RUMBLE Low-frequency noise caused by a tape transport mechanism.

SELECTIVITY A tuner's ability to distinguish between stations spaced closely together on the dial.

SEPARATION The degree to which channels are kept apart. A difference of 35 dB or more in channel separation normally is considered desirable for high fidelity listening.

SIGNAL An electrical replica of actual sound.

SIGNAL-TO-NOISE (S/N) The proportion of signal to extraneous noise in a hi-fi or similar device. The higher the S/N ratio, measured in decibels, the better.

THD The abbreviation for total harmonic distortion.

TONE CONTROL A means of adjusting the level of bass, midrange, or treble frequencies with respect to the overall sound level.

TWEETER A high-frequency loudspeaker specifically designed to reproduce treble frequencies.

WATT The unit of electrical or acoustical power. The electrical wattage of an amplifier describes the power it can develop to drive a loudspeaker. Acoustical wattage describes the actual sound pressure level a loudspeaker can deliver.

WOOFER A loudspeaker driver specifically designed for bass-frequency reproduction.

WOW Slow, regular variations in the speed of a turntable or tape transport that can cause audible variations on musical pitch.